AIDS AND YOUNG PEOPLE

Other titles in this series:
   Drugs and Young People by Grahame Knox
   The Occult and Young People by Roger Ellis
   Sex and Young People by Lance Pierson

AIDS and Young People

Dr Patrick Dixon

KINGSWAY PUBLICATIONS
EASTBOURNE

Copyright © Patrick Dixon 1989

First published 1989

All rights reserved.
No part of this publication may be reproduced or
transmitted in any form or by any means, electronic
or mechanical, including photocopy, recording, or any
information storage and retrieval system, without
permission in writing from the publisher.

Front cover photo: Mick Rock, Cephas Picture Library

British Library Cataloguing in Publication Data

Dixon, Patrick
 Aids and young people.
 1. Man. AIDS—Christian viewpoints
 I. Title
 261.8'321969792

 ISBN 0-86065-670-5

Production and printing in Great Britain for
KINGSWAY PUBLICATIONS LTD
Lottbridge Drove, Eastbourne, E Sussex BN23 6NT by
Nuprint Ltd, 30b Station Road, Harpenden, Herts AL5 4SE.

To My Parents

Contents

	Foreword	9
1.	AIDS Is Your Problem Too	11
2.	What Is AIDS?	24
3.	Newsflash on Cures, Vaccines and Condoms	32
4.	Take Care of Yourself	49
5.	Agony AIDS	58
6.	Nowhere to Go	73
7.	What Do You Think?	86
8.	Where Are You Going?	110
9.	Time for Action	122
	Helpline	126

Foreword

Life After AIDS

What you are about to read is perhaps the most important thing you will ever learn about your body and the way it works. The future of the next generation will depend on whether or not you and others in your situation take seriously the message of this book and do something about it.

Stories of people in this book have been disguised and adapted to protect identity.

Abbreviations used:
AIDS   Acquired Immune Deficiency Syndrome
HIV   Human Immune-deficiency Virus

I
AIDS Is Your Problem Too

Unless something changes, within a few years every person who picks up a copy of this book will probably know personally someone who has died because of AIDS. It may be an older brother or sister, a cousin, an uncle, a friend, a man in the same street, a shopkeeper, or someone at school or at work. You may not realise it because AIDS is kept so secret. You may think the person died of cancer, but someone somewhere knows otherwise.

Some people freak out. They turn the telly over whenever AIDS is mentioned. They get scared if they think someone at the party last night had the disease. They panic about the thought of touching someone with AIDS or picking up a dirty glass without realising and drinking from it. If they actually think several people may have been infected, then panic turns to hysteria.

Ambulance men in 'space-suits'

Police turn up wearing gloves, masks and overshoes to arrest a suspect, in case he is infected. Ambulance men turn up to transport someone who could have AIDS wearing 'space-suits'. A priest offers someone Holy Communion wearing gloves, with a bit of bread stuck on the edge of a wooden spatula. Old ladies in churches go back to their seats without drinking the wine. Meals-on-wheels delivery service of a hot meal to the home of someone who is ill becomes a stone-cold meal left on the doorstep because the driver is too scared to ring the bell and go inside. All these things and worse have happened recently in the UK.

Fear soon turns to anger. Bricks fly through windows or the house is burnt to the ground (this has happened twice recently in London). People are sacked on the spot and thrown out of their homes. And the problem keeps on growing.

Bored rigid with AIDS

Most people I meet are bored rigid with AIDS—until they meet someone who has it. It is a terrible shock to find your best friend is dying. It is even worse when you find that no one will talk about it because he has the wrong disease. He doesn't have cancer, and it is as if he has ceased to exist. No one wants to know.

AIDS is the silent killer because by the time you know you've got it it's too late. But the trouble is that HIV is spreading fast and in spite of what you have been told, most of the people infected worldwide are neither gay men nor drug addicts, although it is true that in this country those two groups have so far been the first to get it. I have been to places abroad where half of all the young people in the town are dying or likely to die—both men and women.

People aren't worried about AIDS because no one they know is dying. But the problem is that by the time you know one friend who is ill, you will probably know a hundred people who are infected and going to die in the future. There is a big time delay. For example, a man who died in a hospice a few months ago in London, last had sex in 1980.

Chain reaction

People you see on the TV, or read about in the papers, may have been infected in the late 1970s before anyone had even heard of AIDS. For the last five to ten years they have felt completely well and probably have been exposed to a number of other risky situations where, unknown to them, they may have passed on the infection. Each person may infect another in a long chain reaction.

One year only two people in a club are infected, but within ten months the number has risen to four. By the time another year is up the number has risen to eight and a year later it reaches sixteen. Everyone is well and looking fit. No one has even the remotest idea that anything is wrong.

After another year-and-a-half forty in the club are doomed, and a year later almost 100. And then a well-known member of the club has a mysterious viral illness and is out of action for six weeks. When he returns he looks really tired, but within a week or two he is back in action again. Six months later his friends notice that he has lost some weight, and one night after dinner he is rushed off to the hospital because he can't breathe. He had been a bit short of breath over the last few days and had a cough, but nothing more.

One of his mates turns up to see him the next day to find he has died in intensive care of pneumonia. A week later his brother tells someone in the bar that the doctors suspect he died of AIDS. That same night the 102nd person in the club took a risk with someone he thought he knew was 'safe' and became infected. So if you know that ten people in your city or town have died of AIDS, you know that maybe up to 1,000 are walking around the streets every day feeling fine but carrying the killer virus.

Spreading like wildfire

In every country of the world each person with HIV has on average infected one other person within a few months. The time it takes for one to infect two to infect four to infect eight to infect sixteen and so on, is called the 'doubling time'. A common cold spreads fast, and has maybe a doubling time of about a week.

So on the first day of term one person has a cold. Over the following weeks the numbers only rise slowly at first: one, then two, then four, then eight, then sixteen, then thirty-two. After the fifth week of term something dramatic happens and sixty-four new people go down with a cold. The week after it is even worse and 128 are sniffing and sneezing. After another week 256 are feeling rotten and the week after that 512 want to have a day off.

Actually it is not quite that bad. If 512 people have now been infected, only 256 will still be sneezing because a cold only lasts one week and the rest were infected over a week ago and have got better. If the school has 1,000 pupils then in a couple more weeks you might expect that everyone has had the cold. This never happens because some people, for reasons we don't understand, will manage not to get it at all.

The way the cold spread through the school shows you how HIV can spread—but with one or two important differences. With HIV the doubling time is not a week but usually starts off in a country at around six months. After thousands of people have been infected, the doubling time slows down, as it would have done in the school. When there are only 100 people left in the school who have not already had the cold, or are able to fight it off, then the numbers getting it each week will suddenly fall—say 256, then 512, then 100, then fifty, then ten, then one. A week later no one in the school has that particular cold.

Injecting death

It is true, however, that while the spread of HIV through sexual contact is relatively slow, because most people do not swop partners every day of every week, the spread from injecting drugs can be extremely fast, with one addict infecting at least one other every day. In this situation the numbers of people infected could go over a period of weeks from one, to two, to four, to eight, to sixteen, to thirty-two, to sixty-four, to 128, to 256, to 512 to over 1,000. This is why Italy, New York, parts of Scotland and other places with a bad drugs problem now have such a terrible AIDS problem.

Like the school cold, the virus causing AIDS spreads from one person to another until most of the people who are at risk from getting it have got it, and then the spread slows down. If the virus hits a nightclub where there is a lot of casual sex, then the virus will spread quickly until most of the people who have multiple partners have got it. After that the chances are that people are just reinfecting each other and no one new is getting it. The virus has been trapped by the small network of relationships. But if two infected club members go to other parts of the country, or to another club the other side of town, they have just given the virus free transport to another group of uninfected people where it can start to spread again.

AIDS is not a 'gay disease'

In this country the virus first spread among the gay community. After a while people within those local groups started to die and testing showed that thousands had been infected. Panic stopped a lot of risky sex, so although maybe only one in four of some groups were infected, the rest took themselves out of sexual circulation and the virus had few new places to go. In the gay community the pattern is like that in a school with a cold: between 1982 and 1984 the numbers infected rose from four in 100 to twenty-one in 100, but the spread has since slowed right down.

Because the people dying today were those people infected at around that time or earlier, many people look at those dying and think that the disease only affects gay men and that it is still spreading rapidly among them. As we have seen, this is almost certainly untrue, but what *is* true is that the virus is taking every opportunity to jump from one group to another. For example, this is happening through gay men who are also having sex with women, through the partners of those with a drug habit, through prostitution and through any other group of friends who don't mind taking risks.

Could the whole world die?

AIDS is unlikely to wipe us all out. Within any group, town or nation it spreads rapidly through those most at risk, it spreads more slowly through those at medium risk and spreads very slowly through those at low risk. How many people are infected, and how quickly, depends quite simply on how many people there are in each of those groups. If we can persuade people to change from high-risk living to low-risk living, then we can at least slow down the spread. Better still, if we can persuade enough people to change to no-risk behaviour, those who do not may still eventually need care as they get ill and die, but the vast majority who change in time will be able to protect themselves from a similar fate.

Who is 'safe'?

In Italy they talk about AIDS as a plague of drug addicts. In Africa it is known as a plague of men and women. In the UK at the moment it is known mainly as a plague affecting the gay community...but all that is changing. AIDS is a disease of relationships and the virus causing it spreads along the lines of relationships. It spreads through a pub, a nightclub, a factory, an office, a youth club and a school. It is pot luck as to which particular geographical area and group it hits first.

One thing is sure: AIDS knows no boundaries of nation, colour, personality or sexual orientation. The virus crosses between sexes and between people of the same sex when they have sex together, or when blood or secretions from one person enter the bloodstream of another.

In the UK, as in the USA, the first group to be badly affected was the gay community. As we have seen, one group only has to be hit a few years earlier than another to have a problem 100 times greater. That creates a misleading impression that you only really develop AIDS if you are a member of that group.

France has twice as many people with AIDS as the UK. So you might conclude that French people have twice as many sexual partners, or twice as many drug injectors. Not at all. The explanation is simple. AIDS possibly entered France about ten months before it entered the UK. In ten months' time we will have as many dying of AIDS as there are in France today.

Heads in the sand

People say that AIDS will never affect people outside the gay community. They are very foolish. Whenever plagues have threatened towns, cities or nations there have always been some who acted like ostriches. By the time you see a number of heterosexual people die of AIDS in the UK, a vast spread of silent infection will have happened.

People always think they are safe until it is too late—and governments are no exception. In San Francisco they knew all about this strange new disease called AIDS that killed young men in New York and Los Angeles. They were worried and started to look for signs of spread into their own community. They missed it. By the time they realised they had a problem, one in four of the entire gay community was already infected.

'It could never happen here'

In the UK the story is the same. In 1983 various experts started to get worried that the virus causing AIDS could be carried in the blood. Haemophiliacs are people who bleed very easily because their blood lacks special ingredients to make it thicken and clot when they cut themselves. Without regular injections of blood extracts from many blood donors, they would soon bleed to death from a minor cut. So were they likely to become infected with HIV? The factories that made the extracts were in the USA.

Our government announced that it had taken careful advice and that there was no evidence that haemophiliacs were at risk. Two years later the government was horrified to discover that three out of five children and adults with severe haemophilia in the UK had not only been in great danger, but were actually now already infected. A disaster had happened under their noses. No one had died or had been ill. The silent killer had spread quietly so that now 250 children were likely to die. By the time they realised, it was too late.

That is why I am not very impressed with the same old 'it will never happen here' when talking about young people today. In parts of central Africa it seems that one in five of all the young men and women are already doomed by the virus. We now know that AIDS was around in Africa, as in the USA, back as early as the 1960s. People were dying, but even with all the medical teams alerted, we only realised there was a single case of AIDS in Africa in 1983. In that year we suddenly began to realise the silent disaster in central Africa. It was possible that tens of thousands had already perished, and millions were already infected. For them it was too late.

Worse than a war

And now the USA government admits that at least 1,500,000 are infected in their country. If everyone infected survived only six weeks, the USA would be in national mourning and the economy would be in a state of collapse. There would be mass panic. Vietnam wiped out 50,000 American young men from the US army over ten years. AIDS makes those deaths look almost insignificant. Even if there is not a single new infection in the USA after the moment you buy this book, the death toll will be the equivalent of twenty Vietnam wars.

In the UK around 250 young men died in the Falklands War. The government's own figures are that even if there is not a single new infection in the UK, the death toll is likely to be greater than 200 Falklands wars. Even more alarming is that the government reckons that up to fifty new people were infected today. The loss of life over the the next few years from those infected this week alone will be the equivalent of a Falklands war once a week or a Kings Cross fire disaster once a day. We think around 60,000 people are infected in the UK.

So who is safe?

You are safe from AIDS if you are not infected yourself and are faithful to one partner, who is also not infected at the moment and remains loyal to you and does not take risks with injecting.

Life will never be quite the same again

In 1988 life insurance rates for young men trebled and for young women they doubled. Big companies are scared that they will go bust because of AIDS. They are right to be scared. In new York, AIDS is soon to become the biggest cause of lost years of life and is already the most common killer of young women between twenty-five and thirty-four years old. Lung cancer tends to kill people who are getting on and would anyway die of something else before too long. AIDS hits you at the peak of your life. In New York they reckon half a million young people are going to die of AIDS.

Everything is changing. Fashions are changing. No one in New York wants to be slim any more because people with AIDS often lose weight. Fat is back. Large people are healthy people. Fad diets are out and people are more cautious about having casual sex.

Nothing new about AIDS?

Sex diseases have been around for thousands of years. Syphilis infected and killed tens of thousands of people until a treatment was found forty years ago. Gonorrhoea has continued to spread rapidly and is now often resistant to our drugs. We have a big problem with herpes which causes painful blisters making sex impossible. It comes and goes for life. There is no cure.

Cancer of the neck of the womb (cervix) is becoming more common because you are more likely to get it if you first have sex as a teenager and have a number of different partners. More and more women are also finding they can't have children. This is increasingly because of sex diseases which damage a woman inside. Usually she doesn't realise until the damage is done.

The great sex age is over

In the 'swinging sixties' people talked a lot about sexual liberation once the pill meant that a woman was safe from getting pregnant. In the seventies and eighties there has been an explosion of sexual activity among young people, and the number of young people needing treatment for sex diseases has soared.

We are now living with the results of the sex age where long-term relationships have not been as important as having a good time tonight, where many people have stopped thinking twice before jumping into bed together or before cheating on each other, and where marriage built on faithfulness has often become meaningless.

But what has it all left us with? Our so-called 'wonderful' sex age has left us with millions of casualties; young people who have grown up in households that have fallen to pieces because a parent has had several partners. You don't have to be a doctor or a child psychiatrist to see what a disaster it has been for so many today.

People are also having second thoughts because of AIDS.

2

What is AIDS?

No one dies solely of AIDS

AIDS is a condition when a particular virus has weakened your body so other germs can invade and kill you. That's what the name 'AIDS' means: your body is usually very good at destroying germs. We call this immunity. When your immune defences are badly damaged, we say you are suffering from an immune deficiency. Some people are born with bad immune systems and others acquire a deficiency because of a disease. Because AIDS is acquired through an infection, we call it the Acquired Immune Deficiency Syndrome (AIDS for short).

HIV just stands for Human Immune-deficiency Virus, which is the scientific name for the virus which causes AIDS.

Whatever names we use, one thing is important and that is to realise that there are stages from being infected, where a person is an infectious carrier but well, through to early symptoms, and then finally to more severe illness or death. Most people seem to progress from one stage to the next, although the time taken is very variable, as we shall see, and the whole process could take ten years or more.

What is a virus?

A virus is just like a robot or a computer program. It simply contains some written directions to teach cells in your body how to make more viruses. A virus is made up of a bag of protein with a small strip of genetic code inside it. This is like the code that makes your hair brown, your nose short and your ears the shape they are. Everything inside you is programmed by these genes, and amazingly almost every cell in your body has inside it all the instructions to make a complete carbon copy of you!

The code inside the virus only contains one or two instructions, but wrong ones. If the virus sticks for more than a moment onto the outside of a special type of white blood cell, the virus bursts like a tiny bubble, squirting the lethal code into the cell. Within a few minutes the cell has taken a copy inside the cell brain (nucleus) and the cell brain has been permanently reprogrammed. This cell is doomed.

Killing off the soldier cells

For a few weeks or months, or even for a few years, the infected soldier cell keeps floating around in the blood, or swimming between the tissues of your body. The cell has one aim in life: locate and destroy germs. There are hundreds of different germs and each has a different shape, so your body has hundreds of different types of white soldier cells to locate and destroy them. A white cell ready to kill a particular cold germ won't have long to wait, but a white cell programmed to kill cholera could have to wait a lifetime and may never be needed.

Some of your soldier cells could be reprogrammed by HIV, but the question is which ones? You might be lucky and they might be ones which you don't need, but on the other hand....

When a soldier cell meets the right shaped germ it springs into action. After being sleepy for years it works overtime to help produce antibodies. These fit exactly onto the outside of the germ and destroy it. But if the cell has been reprogrammed, the mechanism gets jammed. The new program jumps into action and tells the cell to stop helping to make antibodies. Instead it starts to make new viruses. The cell gets sicker as it gets larger. Eventually it bursts, showering millions more virus particles into the blood. Each one stays in the blood for only a few minutes before it touches a fresh healthy white cell, bursts, injects the code and reprogrammes new cells—soldier cells and braincells, for example.

Why you get ill

Only certain kinds of soldier cells get attacked by the virus, but as they get fewer and fewer it gets harder and harder for your body to kill certain germs. You are fine with ordinary coughs and colds. Most common germs are quickly destroyed, but one or two just keep on growing. The result is a strange chest infection that doesn't respond to antibiotics, or a bad attack of thrush in the mouth, or strange skin rashes, or loose motions caused by infection inside your bowel.

Some of these infections simply cause you to feel run down or to lose weight, but the chest infections can kill and are very hard to treat. No one dies solely of AIDS. You die largely because of the other infections that take over your body when your defences are damaged, or from cancers related to HIV.

How HIV affects people

Jimmy

Eight years ago Jimmy, who is a married man, had sex with another man while on holiday. He didn't know about AIDS—the disease was hardly known and had not even been given a proper name. About six weeks later he felt dreadful. He ached all over and had a temperature. He took himself to bed with a hot water bottle and paracetamol, and two days later put it all down to flu and went back to work. Five years later he noticed a bruise on his left leg, but it wasn't painful and he could not remember banging it. After a month it was still there and his wife noticed another on his back.

Glands had come up in his neck and he felt unwell. Whatever his wife cooked had to be thrown away. Even beer down at the pub tasted awful. When he started getting the runs he began to worry and went to see his doctor. These strange skin marks were appearing all over the place now. They rushed him to a clinic for sex diseases which was a terrible shock. They took him on to the ward and did a huge number of tests. Everyone was talking in the corridors. It was then that he started to get really scared. He was convinced it was cancer.

Eventually a doctor came and sat on the bed and told him he had AIDS, that AIDS had attacked his skin with a kind of cancer called Kaposi's sarcoma, and that he would need special treatments. Jimmy was in a state of shock for weeks. He refused to see any visitors except his wife. He was terrified that people at work would find out. He was now on the AIDS ward. Anyone who rang the hospital to find out about him was bound to realise. Jimmy wanted to kill himself. He tried the first weekend he was allowed out. He felt so ashamed and humiliated. He could not face seeing the children. He felt people were staring at him in the streets. It was bad enough for someone to suspect you might be gay, but this was a living hell. It was like having a photograph of him having sex with that man so many years ago splashed over the front page of all the local papers.

Two years later, after many treatments and hopes, Jimmy was weak and deteriorating fast. At home, he would get up for an hour or two each day before retiring exhausted. He was now thin and a feather would have pushed him over. He had a terrible racking painful cough and was too short of breath to manage the stairs. One night he woke up fighting for breath. His wife was scared and didn't know what to do. She dialled for an ambulance and he died on the AIDS ward later that week.

Maria

Maria never really knew her father. Sometimes in the days before she died she thought she could see him and called out to him. Her mother had married again when she was three years old. By the time she was twelve her stepfather had seduced her several times. He told her it was all right, and their little secret. She hated him for it. She felt too ashamed to tell her mother, although she guessed her mother knew. When she was sixteen she ran away from home with a boy she knew. Within a year she had tried most of the drugs money can buy in London and decided she liked just one. Her boyfriend gave her what she craved for and she gave him what he wanted. When she had to do it for other men, she did it for money and the money was for him and he gave her what she needed.

Five times she had been arrested for loitering, and had been three times in Holloway. And then came two shocks. The first shock was that she was pregnant and the second was that when the baby was born they tested it to see if it had been exposed to HIV. The result was positive. They tested her and she had signs of infection too. They counselled her and let her out. She had nowhere to go. No friends in the world except the friends whom she knew from the street. Within a week she was back to the old routines. The telephone kiosk stickers, the hanging around, the hassling for money and the quick fix. Sex comes more expensive without a condom, but most people will pay the extra. Anyway, why bother when the damage is done? They know the risk and they make their own choices.

A year later she was back in Holloway again, in reception for her medical before admission. She was ill and she knew it. People passed her by in the street. She wore a wig now because her hair was so thin. Her mouth was really sore and her eyes were red. She was covered in a dry itchy rash which drove her mad at night. She was getting forgetful and her boyfriend had started hitting her again. With any luck this time she would be in the medical block. Next week she would hit the streets again. Another man, another fix. Within a year she was dead.

Karen

Karen cried for two weeks when she was told. She had slept with him only twice in six months. The first she knew she had AIDS was when she landed up in hospital with a chest infection which nearly killed her. After six weeks she was home, on special drugs which she had to remember to take every few hours. Within a month she had needed her first blood transfusion and had felt really run down. She had told her parents. Her mother was understanding, but she could not talk to her dad. It was like he was looking straight through her. An old schoolfriend had been wonderful. She was learning to manage the diarrhoea quite well when she had a second chest infection and died on the ward.

Thomas

Thomas was a thirty-seven-year-old machine operator. He was highly skilled, but several times recently he had nearly wrecked the equipment. Sometimes he forgot to do important things and he noticed he was getting clumsy. When he started to feel generally unwell and began to lose weight, he went to a special clinic for a check-up. It wasn't long before they started to talk to him about having a test to see if he had been infected with the AIDS virus. He refused, but when he suddenly developed pneumonia and was rushed to hospital, he wasn't surprised when they told him he had AIDS.

Although he recovered from the pneumonia he became quite lethargic, depressed and withdrawn. He would spend much of the day curled up on the sofa with a rug over him. He tried to go to work, but nearly sliced his fingers off and had to be sent home. He wasn't eating or looking after himself very well and kept falling over. He was also troubled by terrible itching and scratched himself so badly he made himself bleed. His friends were beside themselves with worry and arranged for him to be admitted to a hospice.

His sight began to deteriorate over the next few weeks so that he could no longer read and he was shocked to realise that he was losing control over his bowels and bladder. Six weeks later he lapsed into a coma and died peacefully on the ward.

3
Newsflash on Cures, Vaccines and Condoms

Almost every week it seems we read or hear about some new wonder cure for AIDS. They say someone has already found a vaccine, and they also tell us how sex is safe if you use a condom. These things are good news if they are true—but are they?

A lot of what you read and hear is rubbish. If it was as easy as some people make out to find a cure, or if a good vaccine really had been found, doctors, nurses, hospitals and governments could stop worrying. The reason why there is so much fuss about preventing the spread of infection is because the truth is that there is no cure, nor is there one anywhere in sight. There is no vaccine that works, nor is there likely to be one for at least ten years. To make it worse, condoms are much less safe than some people think they are.

Why there is no cure

I hope that soon we will have a drug that kills viruses and is safe. When that happens, we will have a cure for flu, the common cold, polio, hepatitis, herpes and many other illnesses such as glandular fever; as well as a cure for AIDS. At the moment it is a long way off. In order to understand why this germ is so hard to beat we need to look at another kind of germ.

Until the middle of the second world war tuberculosis was a major killer worldwide, and thousands of people died of pneumonia in this country alone each year. If you had been born fifty years ago, there would have been quite a risk of you dying before your first birthday. If you survived until you were old enough to go to school, you would have noticed the missing places that should have been your brother or sister, cousin, friend or neighbour. Pneumonia wiped out more young children in our country in ten years than Hitler did in the concentration camps.

Miracle cures

Then someone called Alexander Fleming made an amazing discovery in a laboratory: he had taken some germs (bacteria) from a wound and spread them over a saucer full of a special jelly to encourage them to grow. He wanted to have a look at these germs under the microscope. Bacteria need warmth, food, shelter and gas to breathe, and this little saucer was an ideal home for them.

Usually by the following morning he could see lots of white blobs on the jelly. Each blob was a little colony of millions of germs that had grown from just one that had landed on the jelly. Germs grow fast in the right place. But one morning something very strange happened: Fleming noticed that while most of the saucer was covered in colonies, there were a couple of areas where nothing had grown. As he looked more closely he saw that a fungus—presumably floating down onto the saucer from the air in the room—was growing in these gaps.

Animals and humans make waste products from the air they breathe and the food they eat. These waste products contain poisons and need to be got out of the body. Bacteria and fungi are the same. Some of these wastes are very poisonous indeed, so germs growing in your body can make you very ill. Fleming realised that he was watching one germ poisoning another.

He was very excited when he managed to collect some of the poison in a flask and feed it to animals, because he found that it didn't make them ill at all. So now he had a weapon that he could put into the bloodstream of someone who was ill. The weapon would leave whatever was human alone and only kill bacteria. This new medicine (an antibiotic) was called penicillin and led to a large number of similar drugs.

So what about AIDS?

With AIDS we have a big problem. Unfortunately it is not caused by bacteria. As we have seen, bacteria need food and so on in order to grow. Because they are made of completely different building blocks than human cells we can design things that damage and kill these germs alone. AIDS is caused by a virus and as we saw in the last chapter, viruses don't need gas to breathe or food to eat. Viruses are not alive. To make matters worse, nearly all the building blocks that make up a virus which attacks humans, are made in human cells and are made up of human chemicals.

Although we do have many poisons which destroy viruses, they also kill people. We have one or two drugs which are relatively harmless, but they are not very powerful and usually only slow down production of more virus in the body. The main drug used for AIDS is called Zidovudine (or AZT), but it can have a poisonous effect on the bone marrow, causing a need for blood transfusions. It is not a cure, but does prolong life. It is very expensive, it can make you feel very ill and is only available to those who live in wealthy western countries. In some parts of Africa, people with AIDS are lucky to get hold of a packet of aspirin, let alone a drug which costs twenty-five years' wages for one person for a year. And it doesn't even stop you dying.

Easier to land on the moon

I am sure that one day we will manage to find a cure for AIDS, but it is a long, long way off. At the moment we don't have the technology to do it. Making a cure will involve us inventing some amazing tools that will allow us to work inside individual cells in the body. Landing a man on the moon or even on Mars is very simple compared to the skills needed to find a cure. The person who finds a cure will go down in history books as one of the greatest inventors of all time. Books will be written about him or her well into the twenty-second century.

In the meantime you will read of hundreds of false 'cures'. The trouble with AIDS is that people who have it don't actually die of AIDS alone. As we have seen, they die of the infections and problems that come in when AIDS has weakened the body. Anything that helps the body get rid of these other infections can help someone make a dramatic recovery. They go home looking well, and are sometimes still completely well some months later. Until they get another chest infection, people think they have been cured. This gives rise to rumours and false reports:

'I took this special antibiotic and within a day I was out of hospital and haven't looked back since. I don't have AIDS any more.'

The first comment is right, the second is wrong. The person could die quite quickly at any time. The soldier cells are getting weaker and weaker, and with each passing day the body is more and more wide open to new germs. Although the person may be looking well he is sitting on a time-bomb.

Rubbish cures

In Uganda recently, drugs for tuberculosis were being talked about as a cure for AIDS. Nonsense. People with AIDS are especially likely to die of tuberculosis. The drug kills tuberculosis, not AIDS. In the USA, treatments for syphilis are being called treatments for AIDS. They are not—they help people recover from syphilis alone.

Some people are pushing fad diets, wholemeal foods, vitamins in large doses, exercise, sleep and psychotherapy in varying combinations as a cure for AIDS. What value do these things have?

It is true that if your soldier cells aren't working too well then anything that helps your immunity is going to help keep you healthy, and things which make you run down and prone to being ill should be avoided. Common sense tells you to take care of yourself: eat proper regular meals, take some exercise, keep your weight reasonable, eat plenty of fresh fruit, cut out the smoking, cut down on alcohol and stop all other recreational drugs, and make sure you get enough sleep. These low-cost measures are likely to prolong the life and well-being of most people and especially of those with AIDS or the early infection.

However, some people, especially in the West Coast, USA, are advertising all kinds of very expensive and useless remedies. A lot of people are making a lot of money out of AIDS.

What about a vaccine?

Vaccines are our only weapon against viral diseases. Polio, whooping cough, measles and other illnesses are becoming more rare now thanks to vaccines. A worldwide programme against smallpox has now succeeded in wiping it off the face of the earth. So why not AIDS?

A vaccine is made by giving you a germ that is harmless but is the same shape on the outside as the disease germ. Within a week you will develop special antibodies to get rid of it. The first time it always takes longer. The next time you meet the same germ it takes only an hour or two to get your soldier cells into battle. Your soldier cells can remember a germ they have met before several years ago.

If you now meet a completely different and dangerous germ, and the shape is the same as a germ your body has met previously, your body is well prepared, and instead of dying of polio, for example, you feel slightly unwell and get better in a day or two. The vaccine has made you immune.

Master of disguise

The trouble with AIDS is that the virus keeps changing its shape so it confuses the soldier cells. A vaccine you give someone today might protect him next week, but what about next month? Here we have a virus that is immune to your soldier cells. That is why your body can virtually never get rid of it. There are other viruses that change shape as well. You may have wondered why flu is still a major cause of lost days at work or at school, or why all our skills are defeated by the common cold.

The reason is that both of these illnesses are caused by viruses that tend to look a bit different every time you meet them. By the time you have passed your cold on to a friend, and it has been passed on another few dozen times, it has travelled halfway round the world, infected maybe 10,000 people in total, and has altered shape. Each person infected makes new viruses inside their nose cells and sometimes the viruses coming out are not exactly the same shape as the virus that came in.

A year or two later you meet someone with a cold—the same cold you had before. If the virus was like measles or chickenpox, your body would have remembered it and killed it straight away. But the virus looks so different on the outside that when the soldier cells get their picture library out they just can't identify it. There is no pre-made antibody that is a good enough fit, so the soldier cells have to start all over again and by the time those antibodies are ready you have been wandering around for a whole week clutching a soggy handkerchief and feeling sorry for yourself.

If you go to your doctor with flu or a bad cold, he just tells you it is a self-limiting illness, which is his complicated way of telling you that there is no cure and no vaccine that can help and you just have to wait for your soldier cells to get going.

A vaccine for flu

There is a vaccine for flu and it just about works because the virus tends to stay the same shape for a bit longer than the cold virus. We have a look at what's coming round the corner from the other side of the world. We take samples from people in Hong Kong and Australia and we know that if we can get the vaccines made and give it quickly to old people in the UK then we may be able to reduce the number of flu deaths this winter. But you have to have a new vaccine each year.

So even if we do find a vaccine for AIDS which is safe and works, we will probably have to revaccinate everyone at frequent intervals. The virus may still not be destroyed. It can change shape in small ways even in the same person over a few weeks, so antibodies that were a good fit at the beginning of the month are almost useless by the end of the month.

A virus dressed up to look like you

There is another problem (as if things were not bad enough already). The antibodies which soldier cells make have to have something on the outside of the virus to hang onto: some bump or handle shape. The coating of cells from a cow looks and feels quite different to the coatings of another animal. Human cells have a special feel to them as well. Soldier cells know exactly what your own cells feel like. If they didn't they would get confused and attack your heart cells or your skin cells or some other part of you, thinking it was an enemy.

When any germ enters the body, the soldier cells have a good look at it and check it against their list of friendly cells. They soon recognise an enemy and destroy it. The trouble with the HIV virus is that it is a wolf dressed up in sheep's clothing. When the new viruses are made, they come out of the cell like tiny buds which break off. Each little round virus is carefully coated with a piece of human cell wall as it comes out. So when a soldier cell meets the virus, it thinks the virus is a friendly human cell, part of your own body.

There are a few unfamiliar odd shapes that stick out like bristles. These are the only things the soldier cells see as non-human to be destroyed. The trouble is that after the soldier cells have gone to all the trouble of making antibodies that fit, the antibodies hang onto the bristles to try and stop the virus and destroy it, but the bristles fall off, allowing the virus to float off down the bloodstream unharmed. These bristles can also change shape as we have seen.

Depressing news

Whatever you may read, the truth is that we have never yet found a single human antibody that is powerful against HIV—even if it is exactly the right shape. Almost everyone who is infected produces antibodies, but they still get ill and die. This virus is immune to antibodies.

So when you next hear of some wonderful scientist who has given himself a dose of AIDS vaccine, take care. The only way we will know if it works is by giving him an injection of blood from someone who has AIDS and seeing what happens. But how long do you think you will have to wait to be absolutely sure that he will never develop AIDS? Possibly ten years. Until then his wife and children will be living in suspense, knowing that he might die, and also that he may be an infectious carrier.

Give him a test?

You may ask why we can't give him an AIDS test. Unfortunately, the AIDS test is nothing of the sort. It is extremely difficult to detect this tiny virus. The only widely available test we have at the moment is not for the virus itself, but for the antibodies that almost all infected people make. So people wanting a test often have to wait a while after they were last at risk before being tested.

Not everyone ever makes enough antibodies to test positive. You can die because of AIDS even though the test is negative. A negative result is not a complete guarantee that you are all right. However, we can usually get the right answer at least ninety-five times out of 100. If we find antibodies, it means that the person has been exposed to the infection—or that he or she has developed antibodies because of a vaccine. We cannot tell the difference.

Most experts are very depressed when it comes to talking about vaccines. They say that we are almost certainly at least five years from a vaccine that works, and even if we find one it will take years to make sure it is safe enough to give to large numbers of people and to produce at low cost in large quantities.

Condoms are not the whole answer to AIDS

If AIDS kills, the body can't fight it, drugs don't really touch it and vaccines are as good as useless, then what hope is there? Whenever I go into schools or talk to young people they all tell me that safe sex is sex with a condom—even though they may have also decided never to use one. But even if they were to change their minds and to use condoms, do they really work as well as people make out?

The London Rubber Company's profits and turnover have increased considerably due to AIDS: they make latex gloves and they make condoms. But something no one likes to tell you is that condoms may not be as safe as you think they are.

I want to tell you why I say this so you can make up your own mind about who is telling you the truth. Everyone agrees that one major thing more than any other produced the sexual explosion of the swinging sixties, with liberation of women from the fear of pregnancy, the ability to plan a family reliably, and to explore free sexual relationships. The swinging sixties were produced by the pill not the condom.

Condom babies

Before the sixties every mother warned her daughter that if she slept around she could land up with a baby she didn't want. Condoms have been around for years—since 1850 BC (not AD), in fact. The ancient Chinese and the Romans knew all about condoms and they were no more reliable then.

During the second world war condoms were freely available and were the main form of contraception, yet 'war babies', born to women after hasty affairs with soldiers on leave, became a standing joke. Thousands of parents and grandparents and aunts and uncles today were born as 'war babies', or after the war, as 'condom babies'. These were babies that surprised and shocked young girls who thought they were safe from pregnancy because their boyfriends or husbands were wearing condoms.

Even today the success of the latest condoms is not as good as many people think when it comes to reliably preventing pregnancy. If, as a doctor, I have 100 young women patients who have chosen the condom to prevent themselves having babies, then each year I can expect fourteen of the 100 to come into the surgery in a state of shock and confusion because they have missed periods, but just can't believe they are pregnant because their partners were using condoms.

Holey condoms!

Just for the record, condoms on sale which do not have a BSI kitemark have up to seven out of ten with holes in or other faults when you open the packet. Imported brands, even *with* a kitemark, have an average of three in 100 with holes in when they leave the factory. Durex are the best, with only around one in 200 with a hole in *before* you start. But what happens after you open the packet is what is more important. It can be quite difficult to use a condom correctly. Fumbling in the dark it can be torn, it can be caught in a woman's jewellery, it can burst, fall off, roll off and leak if not removed carefully at the end of making love.

If we are honest we have to say that no one is quite sure why condoms have such an appalling habit of letting you down. One good reason may be that people who say they are using them, do buy them with good intentions, but when it actually comes to the heat of the moment they don't get as far as putting them on.

Taking a chance

A recent survey just after the advertising campaigns showed that more young people said they would buy and use condoms. But when the survey was repeated a few months later it showed that the condoms had certainly been bought, but had not been used. When it comes to pregnancy, people are prepared to take a chance—even when a mistake could wreck their entire lives.

Most young people I talk to think the risk of pregnancy is much much greater than the risk of AIDS, and I don't find young people are particularly taking to condoms for any reason. People say they are smelly, slippery, disgusting, spoil any sensation and generally get in the way of what they feel should be something very natural and beautiful.

However, before we start blaming all these unwanted babies on people who can't be bothered to use condoms, we need to look at another large group of people who are very careful, who do not want to have a child at the moment, who always use a good brand but still land up pregnant, presumably because of a small tear, or a hole, or because it slipped off, or for some other reason.

You can get infected even with a condom

If you were to draw a sperm and a virus on the same scale, then if a sperm was ten centimetres long, a virus would be the size of a pinhead. If sperm can cross from a man to a woman, then viruses can too. They can also cross from a woman to a man. It is not surprising then to find that reports are now coming in of men who have infected their wives, or the other way round, with the HIV virus, despite using condoms carefully.

Even if a condom fails, a woman is unlikely to get pregnant. You can only get pregnant on three out of thirty days a month, and even if it happens to be a day when there is an egg around to be fertilised, many people have to try many times before a baby is conceived. In fact five in 100 people will never manage it. Another five in 100 will take months or years of anxious trying before they succeed in having a baby. Mr and Mrs Average take around four months of trying hard.

But with HIV, you can in theory get infected any day of the month. Once can be enough to get it from him or from her.

Condoms are like seat-belts

Seat-belts save thousands of lives a year, but it is feared that because people feel safer wearing them they actually encourage speeding, jumping lights and crazy overtaking. In the end people may land up in riskier situations, and the number of lives saved may not be as great as it should have been.

Condoms are exactly the same: they reduce your chance of dying from an activity which can be highly dangerous. By pushing condoms and making out they are more reliable than they are, the health campaigns have actually been encouraging people not to alter the way they live. 'Carry on as normal, but just remember, when you can, to use a condom.'

It is very simple: if you are going to take a risk by having sex with someone who could be infected (and how will you ever know, since people don't tell the truth and you can't tell by looking) and you don't use a condom, you are crazy. A condom may well save your life. Condoms have without a doubt saved thousands of people from dying of AIDS already. When using condoms, make sure they have the BSI kitemark (a guarantee of the safety level). In conjunction, use a spermicide containing nonoxynol to reduce risk further. If you want to use a lubricant, use those which are water based and contain nonoxynol spermicide. Oil-based lubricants can rot condoms in minutes.

But don't kid yourself that just because you use a condom there will never be a baby or you will never become infected. If you are having sex regularly with someone, or with people who are carrying the virus, then one day, condom or no condom, you may get infected. It is the same as someone who enjoys driving a fast sports car beyond the limits of road safety, thinking he could never be killed in an accident because he always wears a seat-belt. The seat-belt makes him safer—but it does not guarantee he won't get hurt.

You can't have an abortion for AIDS

Condoms reduce the risk by about 85%, but I wouldn't trust my life to a condom. There are already people who are infected or have died despite using them. Condoms are not as safe as some of you think, especially for anal sex. No one ever said they were. All the health literature says that 'for *safer* sex use a condom'. The trouble is that we hear what we want to hear. We hear 'safe'. In a few years time in this country, there will be a lot of angry young people wandering around because they thought they were safe, but are now infected.

As someone said recently, you can abort a baby, but you can't have an abortion for AIDS.

Condoms can be worn by women

There are some new kinds of condoms available now. They are made of the same material as ordinary condoms, but with reinforcement to keep them in place inside a woman. They are very new and experimental, but if properly used could provide an added measure of protection. The trouble is that when a man and woman are actually making love, these very thin membranes of rubber, whether worn by a man or a woman, can slip or move. Things happen, and neither partner is aware until afterwards when it is too late. The stronger and thicker you make these things, the less and less people want to have anything to do with them. The ideal condom is invisible, with neither partner aware at all of anything feeling any different. It doesn't exist, although the female condom may turn out to be an improvement.

As we have seen, AIDS is a terrible disease for which there is no cure and no vaccine. The only hope is to teach people how to protect themselves from infection.

4

Take Care of Yourself

If there is no cure, no vaccine, and condoms merely reduce the risk, what is the answer? Just a few weeks ago I flew with a team to a country where the answer is urgently needed to prevent possibly a whole generation from being wiped out. Uganda has more reported cases of AIDS than any other country in Africa. You might think that means it is the worst affected: it is not. It is certainly the country with the most honest and courageous leaders.

There are several other African nations that almost certainly have as bad a problem, or maybe even worse, who will not speak up. One country has actually reduced the number of AIDS cases it will admit to, even though doctors in that country know the figures are fixed. If people think you have a lot of AIDS then big companies pull out and tourists stop coming. The economy collapses and in addition to having thousands of extra sick young people to look after, you now have high unemployment and increasing poverty.

Young people in Africa

The government of Uganda openly admits there is a big problem. This has opened the doors for international aid and also for education. How can you educate people about a major cause of death when you don't officially admit anyone is actually dying of it?

One church leader we visited has buried twenty members of his church who died from AIDS or 'slim'—so called because people affected lose weight before they die. In the next year a further twenty are expected to die. The year after, he will probably conduct forty funerals, and eighty the year after that—all of them members of his church.

In some parts of central Africa, one in three of all the truck drivers who drive lorries up and down the main highways are infected, and half the young girls who hang around the bars at night. Maybe one in five of all young men and women in some of these towns are infected. Some have said they think there are towns in central Africa where maybe half of all the sexually active young people are dying.

Like any other sex disease

I met a mother who had lost two daughters. Her face was a picture of grief. Composed and dignified, she told me how they had died. 'I wish it had been me,' she said, 'they were so young.' In Africa the infection has always spread like any other sex disease: from man to woman and woman to man. Europeans who stay in these countries often come home infected after having had sex only a few times with prostitutes. At least half of the prostitutes in these countries are infected.

We spoke to over 20,000 people in around ten days, at the request and invitation of the Ministries of Health and Education. When we went into schools and asked for a show of hands from those who knew personally of people who had died because of AIDS, half would put up their hands. If the same question is asked in two years' time I expect it will be everyone.

We held large open-air meetings with a big noisy African band, a huge public address system and interpreters. Thousands attended from local villages. Up to 2,500 people sat in the square or stood motionless, six deep for around three hours, while we assisted the local people in educating and answering questions. Most of the audience were men—hardly ever turning up to such things normally. They came because in the area where we were, AIDS had become a life and death issue for everyone there.

AIDS is big business

But what could we say? Everyone wanted to know about the stories of wonder cures. The truth was that even if there had been one, it would have been too expensive for anyone there. In a post-war economy, basic medicines are available, but anything exotic is like gold dust.

Likewise new vaccines are likely to be tried out on Africans first. Big business interests and the American interest in lawsuits when things go wrong means that Africa is seen in the eyes of some in the West as the ideal place to carry out experiments. But if a vaccine is actually found to work, you can be sure that the last place it will be available in large amounts will be central Africa. Only the other day someone said to me that there were too many people in the world and AIDS was a good way to keep the African population down. I was horrified.

Desperate for a test

Many young people came to me wanting to be tested. They have good reason to be worried. They know there is a very high chance that either of two people about to get married could be infected. If they both are, that is one thing, but if not, then one could kill the other. What should they do? It is quite feeble just to tell them to use condoms carefully for the rest of their lives.

What about children? If the girl has a baby, she knows that the infection can be passed in the milk. She wants to be tested to make sure she does not accidentally kill her baby. A wife came to me. She was worried because her husband was often out with other women late at night. He admitted he had been repeatedly unfaithful over the last ten years, and they both realised that he could easily be infected, like so many of the people he knew who had died. They wanted to know if it was safe for him to sleep with anyone again—let alone his wife.

All these anxious people: they do not only need counselling. Some of them have an urgent need for a test. But at the time of writing, whatever you may read or hear, testing is only available to check blood about to be used for those having operations. Testing for ordinary men and women is impossible. Until it is available the private agonies continue.

One partner for life

The response of the Ugandan government to the crisis has been prompt and impressive. No watered down messages like in the UK. For them the answer is obvious and clear: *'Safe sex is sex between virgins now married for life. (If you really can't manage it a condom might save your life.)'*

In Africa they are very worried too about spread from medical treatments. In some areas one in five pints of blood in the hospital blood banks is full of virus. In some parts of Africa they still don't have the facilities to test all blood. Needles can be in short supply or equipment to heat and sterilise can be broken or unavailable. No one will ever know just how many people doctors and nurses have killed in Africa without knowing it. So an important part of the health campaign has been making sure that everyone is aware of the dangers of blood and needles.

People say Africa is different

A lot of people have tried to think up various reasons why Africa is different. You must make up your own mind. Some said that Africans are especially sensitive to HIV and that is why it spreads so fast. They worked out that answer from experience in a London clinic. For six months that was the answer trotted out around the world, until the red-faced doctors made a public confession that they had wrongly added up the figures.

The next answer given was that Africans are much more promiscuous. People believe what they like to believe. While it is certainly true that some patterns of behaviour encourage multiple sexual partners in parts of Africa, the difference is not enough to explain what is happening.

Another suggestion was that medical treatments with dirty needles and infected blood was the reason. It is easy to make armchair assessments when you are 6,000 miles away. The fact is that if that were true then every age group that receives medical care by injection would be likely to get AIDS, whereas most of those infected are young sexually-active men and women.

Finally, some have suggested that infection first with one disease could open the body to infection by another. We have good reason to think this happens. Common sense tells us that if you are already chronically sick and then you are infected by the AIDS virus, you are not in the best possible shape to fight it. Malaria and other tropical diseases could be responsible.

However, the most likely explanation is other sex diseases. As in the UK, there are a large number of people in central Africa who have picked up sex diseases. However, in much of Africa, there are not many treatment centres and tracing sexual partners of those infected can be hard. We know that if a man or a woman is infected with gonorrhoea or syphilis, the small wounds made by these germs can become easy ways into the body for the AIDS virus.

Already happening here

People say it could never happen here. I'm not quite sure what they mean because it is *already* happening here. It is true that we do not have a vast number of people infected with things like malaria, although those who inject drugs or are practising homosexuals can for reasons of lifestyle have weakened immunity.

It is true that medical treatments in the UK are now almost completely safe, although treatments have so far infected 1,000 adults and 250 children in the UK, and blood transfusions are still infecting one or two people each year. But one drug user in Edinburgh may spread the virus into the bloodstreams of maybe 1,500 others in eighteen months. Through dirty needles the virus is now continuing to spread rapidly to other parts of the UK. In London, which has 10–25,000 injectors of drugs, eight out of fifty are already infected in some areas, and the numbers are rising. In Italy, as we have seen, AIDS has been mainly spread through dirty needles.

It is true that sex diseases tend to be treated more promptly in this country, but we have been seeing an explosive rise in new cases over the last few years, and women in particular often fail to realise they are infected at all because the damage is painless in the earlier stages and is inside.

As in parts of Africa, there is at least one place already in the UK where half of the prostitutes are infected. Men are usually allowed to pay more not to use a condom which most prefer to do. A UK report shows that a prostitute may have sex with several thousand men a year. Infected drug users can easily pass on the infection to their partners, and some have done so.

You can see for yourself that everything that has happened in central Africa is bound to happen to some extent in the West. It is a stupid man who comes back from a detailed look at what is happening in Africa and says AIDS will never spread to affect people other than gay men and drug addicts in the UK.

How can I keep uninfected?

You need to make a decision if you have not already done so, that the next person you have sex with will be the person you are committed to making love to for the rest of your life. Some say life is not that simple. What if that person has had several partners before, or what if you have? What if your partner is unfaithful or is injecting drugs?

The question of testing is a difficult and complex one and every person or couple is different. Where the risk is quite great it may well be worth one or both being tested for the sake of the other. You need expert medical advice from your doctor or from a special clinic. There are also a number of other agencies which give advice. The Freephone 24-hour National AIDS Helpline number is at the back of this book.

The other decision you need to make, if you have not already done so, is never, never under any circumstances to allow yourself to be injected with a needle that could contain traces of someone else's blood.

Zero risk

If you keep to these two very simple things you will reduce your risk to nearly zero. Any remaining risk would be if your partner was continuing to take risks—especially if you are kept in the dark—or if you are in the medical or caring professions. If you fall into this group you should already have clear instructions on how to protect yourself while also giving excellent care. The basic rule is to keep blood and any other body fluids off your skin as far as possible, especially off your hands as there are sometimes small breaks in the skin for the virus to enter.

In the next chapter we look at some of the common worries and problems people have.

5
Agony AIDS

The trouble with AIDS is that most people are far too scared to ask the things they really need to know—but there are exceptions.

A fourteen-year-old girl came up to me after a talk at a school in London. I had to ask the classroom to be cleared and the teacher to leave before she could bring herself to speak. Her friend was by her side holding her arm. Finally she asked: *'If someone has been raped, can that person get AIDS?'* She had a particular person in mind and I wondered if it was herself as a victim of child sex abuse. I had to tell her that there was a risk if the man was infected—especially in rape because the violence could cause tears and bleeding, making entry of the virus into the blood much easier.

'We have a boy who bleeds easily in our school. Can I get the AIDS virus from him? Is he likely to be infected?'

Some people are born with blood that does not thicken when they cut themselves. Scabs and clots do not form, so even a minor scratch, graze or cut continues to bleed for several hours. People can slowly bleed to death and until recently people severely affected used to die as young children. There is no cure. The disease is called haemophilia. It used to be called the Royal Disease because some Royal Families were badly affected. The disease is passed on from parents and if members of the same family marry it is likely that the husband and wife may both be carriers and go on to have children who are severely affected.

We can't make the blood thicken, but we can get the life-saving extracts from the blood of other people. Hundreds of pints of donated blood are needed for one person. The blood extracts were bought from the USA until recently and were contaminated with HIV, although we did not realise this before. As a result, about three out of five people with the most severe form of haemophilia, who needed blood extracts before 1985, are now infected with HIV. This is a terrible tragedy as it affects around 250 school children and 1,000 adults in the UK alone.

The risk is that many of these people will become ill and die over the next few years. However, the risk to you is around zero. We are not going to see an outbreak of AIDS in the classroom because of haemophiliacs. In order for you to become infected you would have to get blood from the cut of someone who is infected into a cut in your own skin. Skin is a massive protection against the virus. If the virus were the size of a ping-pong ball, then the thickness of your skin would be as wide as Wembley football stadium.

'I was walking my girlfriend home the other night and there was this old condom lying in the gutter. People are always leaving them when they drive off in their cars at night. Can you get the AIDS virus from picking one up?'

As more and more people are carrying the virus, it is more and more likely that discarded condoms will be full of virus. Sex in cars is more likely to be sex in a temporary relationship. People who are sticking to just one partner over a long period can usually find more comfortable and private places to make love. So a condom in the gutter is more likely to have been thrown away by people who are having risky sex and again more likely to be a health hazard. It should be picked up and thrown in a bin, wearing gloves, or with a tissue, or a stick, but this is just being sensible.

'My boyfriend says that I don't love him because I don't want to have sex with him.'

One thing is absolutely certain: he doesn't love you—or if he does, he doesn't respect you. If he is pressurising you to give yourself away to him without real commitment on his part, he is more interested in getting pleasure for himself than in building a relationship with you.

'I know my boyfriend and he says he's a virgin too, so it must be safe.'

A man will tell you anything he wants in order to have sex with you, if he wants it enough. The town where you live is full of hurt girls and women who have been badly let down. They agreed to have sex as a way of tying him down, because of fear that the relationship would break up, because he promised that they would get married one day. But he had no intention whatsoever of getting 'trapped for life'.

You may be looking for a home, a husband who will love you, care for you and be a good dad to your children. But your boyfriend may be just looking for a good time, no strings attached, and a relationship he can turn off like a tap when one day he sees someone new or gets bored. In the meantime you will hear everything you have dreamed of hearing: 'I love you. You are the only girl for me. I am committed to you.'

Anyway, even if he is a virgin now, do you really think that he is never going to sleep with any other girl for the rest of his life? Is this really it? Is he really the guy who is never going to look at another girl again? If he is so keen to have sex with you now before any commitment in marriage, he'll be just as keen to try it out with someone else later on, even maybe after he has married you.

'The two of us are getting married next year. We have not had sex together. But both of us, if we're honest, have had a bit of a past. Should we both be tested before we get married?'

This is a really urgent issue for many couples now—especially in Africa where the risks of marrying someone who is infected are enormous. There are a number of people who are asking to be tested for these reasons. I think there is a good case for it. It depends on how big the risk has been. A member of a church came up to me the other day. He had been an injector of heroin until a few years ago when he became a Christian, which changed his entire life and he broke the habit. Should he be tested before going any further?

These questions need expert individual counsel. There is no standard right answer. It depends on three things: firstly, how long ago the risky behaviour took place, because the risk halves with every ten months that passes between then and now. This is because, say five years ago there was only one infected person for sixty infected now, so your risk then was sixty times less than for someone doing the identical thing this week.

Secondly, it depends on what the risky behaviour was and where, because as we have seen, in any given country at a particular time, the disease was mainly confined to particular groups. For example, a man who said he had been sharing needles with drug addicts in Italy around two years ago, is far more likely to have been infected than if he had been sharing in London at the same time. However, sharing anywhere today is dangerous.

Thirdly, it depends on whether or not the person is in a sexual relationship or about to enter into one. If either is the case, which of course it is for someone about to get married, then it could be a matter of life or death for the other partner.

These things need to be carefully talked through, and other factors have to be considered, such as how a positive result could affect your life with regard to life insurance, job, promotion and other things. The best person to talk these things over with is a specialist advisor at a clinic for genito-urinary diseases. Most major hospitals have them, and there are some addresses at the back of this book. You don't need an appointment, and they will respect complete confidence—they have to, otherwise no one would ever go to them.

'I am confused because many people say certain things can give you AIDS and other people say they cannot.'

It is very confusing for people, and most people, most of the time, are more afraid of the stories than anything else. Can I 'get AIDS' from a cup, or what about kissing, or swimming, or mosquitoes or anything else? Before answering all these questions in detail, we need to look at the kind of dangers we put ourselves in every day.

In the middle of a very busy schedule I had to train some volunteers in Dundee last March. The church there kindly offered to fly me up to Edinburgh and collect me from the airport. Someone who was afraid of flying might have told me I should not fly because I might die in a crash. Is the person right? Of course he is. I might well crash, or the plane could even be hijacked. But I still went. Why did I fly? Because it saved a lot of time and the cost was not that much more than the rail fare.

At the end of the day I took a risk because, on balance, the risk was very small and did not mean I needed to change what I did. Each time you travel in a car you could die in a crash, and each time you travel on a bus you could catch flu. You could get bitten by a dog in the park and you could be mugged on the way home from a party. The world can be a dangerous place, but we have to get things in proportion or we would all worry ourselves sick. Some people get overwhelmed by all these things and get so worked up that they cannot go outside the house. They need expert help. Others laugh at them: 'Surely people realise that the risk of something dreadful happening is incredibly small?'

When it comes to AIDS, even the most sensible of us can start behaving in a very odd manner. A grown man leaves a parcel in the rain on the doorstep because he is afraid to ring the bell. A social worker visiting to sort out financial help is afraid to drink her cup of tea. At church people are staying away from communion services because they are afraid of the cup. At a conference very few want to shake the hand of a visiting speaker.

Because our work with people dying of AIDS at home is growing so fast, the team with whom I work needed urgently to find bigger offices earlier this year. After much searching we found somewhere ideal, but the owners were afraid we would pollute the toilets and refused to let us move in.

The trouble is that if I told you that many of these things had absolutely no risk you probably would not believe me. If I told you there was in fact a risk you will probably spend the rest of your life worrying. I am not interested in alarming or comforting you. I do want you to know the facts so you can make up your own mind. So we will now look at a few examples:

'I read in a paper that an expert had said you could get AIDS by eating a restaurant meal. Is this true or not?'

No! I suppose that in theory if an infected waiter was to cut his finger with a sharp knife, and hold his finger while it dripped fresh blood all over your meal, and then after he put it in front of you, as you took your first mouthful, you bit your tongue so blood from the waiter entered through a cut in your mouth, possibly there would be the smallest chance that you could become infected. But it is just as silly as saying you should never fly in a plane in case you crash.

'Is it true that some local authorities have closed their swimming pools to people with AIDS or gay men?'

It is true that some people have been worried about swimming pools, but swimming pools are safe. It is true, as you may have read, that HIV can survive under very exceptional circumstances in tiny amounts, for several days sometimes, outside the human body[1]. However, almost all the virus particles are destroyed within a few hours. I suppose that if someone who was carrying HIV was to walk on a piece of glass beside the pool leaving a trail of fresh blood and someone else was to step on the piece

---

1. Advisory Committee on Dangerous Pathogens report, June 1986 (DHSS).

of glass and tread in the same places, there would be a small risk of infection. Common sense tells us that.

If the risk was large we would have seen outbreaks over the years in swimming pools of other diseases carried in the blood, such as hepatitis B. We have not. You have to consider that even if there is blood on the floor, the chances of it being from someone who is infected are absolutely minute. Blood in the pool itself is diluted so many millions of times that I am sure you would be hard pushed to find a single blood cell, let alone a virus particle. The disinfectants in the pool water also make it more likely that the virus will be quickly damaged and incapable of causing disease.

All my family go swimming regularly and have no more intention of stopping than of never flying on an aeroplane.

'My football coach says we must put strong disinfectant in the bucket used to clean wounds during a game. Is this over the top?'

It is extremely unlikely that you could be infected by this route. No one has ever been infected this way, but common sense and hygiene would suggest that giving the sponge a thorough wash in clean water and disinfectant is a good idea. A strong disinfectant will kill the virus very quickly.

'My coach also says we should wear shin pads so blood cannot pass from one player to another.'

In theory, any contact sport where people are likely to injure themselves could allow one person to infect another, but only if they collide so that one bleeding wound is rubbed into another. We are not going to see an outbreak of infection on the football pitch unless it has come from sex or drugs. Anyway, since the number of people infected in this country at the moment is so low, the chances of actually having someone infected on the pitch in the first place—or anywhere else for that matter—must be small.

'I went to get a tattoo on my arm last week. My friends told me I was stupid because I could get infected with the AIDS virus.'

It is true that you must be careful doing anything that pierces the skin. Tattoos, acupuncture, electrolysis and other beauty treatments, piercing ears and other things can all spread HIV infection, as well as other diseases. Most places are well run. If in doubt, ask them what they do about sterilising their equipment.

'My mum says you can't get the AIDS virus from kissing, but I heard it was in saliva and someone got infected from a bite.'

You are probably both right. The virus that causes AIDS can be found in any body fluid from someone who is infected. It is not always there, and sometimes it is only present in very small amounts. If it is present in saliva, then why don't people get infected from kissing?

The truthful answer is that we don't really know, but this is what we think: for a start it appears that there may be certain things in saliva which attack the virus. Secondly, the virus is often only present in saliva in very small amounts. Thirdly, even if the virus from someone infected does enter your mouth, it is doomed unless it can find a way into your bloodstream very quickly. In a few seconds a waterfall of saliva will flood it out of your cavernous mouth down a huge pipe into an enormous lake of deadly burning acid (your stomach), where the virus will be instantly destroyed and broken up into thousands of tiny pieces to be digested. If it survives in a damaged form without being broken up completely, in a few hours it will be ejected from the other end of the gut and down the toilet.

The only way virus in your mouth could infect you is if there was a wound, a mouth ulcer, or a bleeding gum inside your mouth. To be honest, so many people kiss each other—especially young people going out together—that hundreds of doctors have been looking hard at every single known case of infection to find out how it happened. In all the cases so far throughout the world we have not found one that has been caught from a kiss.

However, it is possible that a human bite from someone infected can infect someone else. We think there may be two cases where this has happened. In the first, a boy is thought to have bitten his brother, and in the second, a girl bit her sister. It is easy to understand why this is different from kissing. After all, the teeth broke through the skin, injecting a small amount of saliva—just as effectively as a snake bite.

'So should I stop kissing my boyfriend?'

Of course not! Although, it is true, if I am completely honest, that if I was young and single and I found out that a girl I was going out with was infected, I probably would not want to give her massive long French kisses!

'Last month I went to stay with my aunt in San Francisco. In all the toilets they have disposable paper toilet-seat covers. Can you get AIDS from a toilet-seat?'

No! The Americans have always been a bit fussy about their 'rest rooms'. This is a bit like the stupid comments about waiters in restaurants. There is only a risk of catching the virus if you sit on a seat covered in blood from a menstruating woman and the blood has contact with your genitalia or any cuts you have. This is hardly very likely (would you sit on such a seat in the first place?), and as far as we know, infection has never ever happened by this route.

'You say that the virus cannot cross the skin, but if that is true, how does it pass from a woman to a man, or the other way round?'

This is another area where, if I am honest, I have to say we don't really know. The skin on the penis of a man, and inside a woman, is certainly sensitive, thin and delicate. It seems likely that many totally painless, harmless, minute cracks appear in the skin of both partners when they make love. These are how the virus enters. As we have seen, any other sex diseases will make the skin much more likely to bleed or be open and increase the risk. Anal sex, where a man inserts his penis into the back passage of another man or a woman, often produces small tears around the inside of the back passage. These can bleed, and the stress on the skin of the man inserting is far greater than in vaginal intercourse. In fact the stresses are so great that at present there is not a single condom manufacturer that has come up with a condom suitable and safe for anal intercourse.

'If the virus comes out in urine, will our rivers and water supply become contaminated?'

Sewage works have been dealing with dangerous germs since Victorian times. Controls are strict to ensure that dangerous substances are not washed out into rivers and streams. The amount of virus anyway is absolutely minute. Some have been worried about untreated sewage being pumped into the sea near seaside towns. The danger is from germs which live in sewage and cause diarrhoea, not from HIV.

'I have heard that mosquitoes have spread AIDS in Africa. Is this true and could I get AIDS from being bitten in this country?'

Millions of people all over the world are worried by this question, and when we were in Uganda recently it was one of the commonest things we were asked about. We are sure that the answer is 'no' in Africa and 'no' anywhere else. If AIDS was being spread by this route then all the areas of Africa worst affected by malaria would be worst affected by AIDS too, because malaria is carried by the mosquito. We would also see that all the different age groups were developing AIDS. All ages, after all, get bitten by mosquitoes. In fact, only young children and sexually-active young people, in the main, have been affected by AIDS, so we are sure that mosquitoes are not the cause. There may be a small connection between AIDS and malaria, but that is because if you are ill from one thing already, then when AIDS strikes, you are hit twice as hard.

The only insect that we think could possibly transmit HIV is the bed bug, because when they grow big and fat they eat and carry a lot of blood, and some of this can be injected into the next victim. However, the amount of blood is still so small that someone has calculated that you would have to be bitten an average of 15,000 times to be infected!

In Africa some of these open-air question-and-answer sessions would last several hours with hundreds of people. At the end what I used to say was this: At the moment people are terrified about all the ways they might get infected without having sex. I do not wish people to be any less terrified of getting AIDS. I just wish they were as terrified of the things they really ought to be terrified about, and not afraid at all of the things which are quite safe. I wish people would be as afraid of sleeping around as they are at the moment of actually setting foot inside the house of someone with AIDS.

In the UK we have a crazy situation where a home-help can be afraid to do the cleaning in case some dust containing the virus goes up her nose, but when she goes home she has sex with the milkman. Milkmen are no more likely to be infected than any other group of people, but she is taking a risk which is much, much greater than the risk in doing the cleaning.

Almost all the questions I am asked by young people concern these same areas of non-sexual spread. I hope you have seen that the vast majority of these risks are very, very small and you do *not* need to alter what you are doing, whereas now is the time, if you have not already done so, to make some radical changes in your sexual behaviour and expectations, and to be *very* careful about anything which pierces your skin.

6
Nowhere to Go

Worse than cancer

It is bad enough being told at the age of twenty-three that you have cancer and are likely to die, but when the disease is AIDS it can seem far worse.

Imagine that you go to your doctor because you have been feeling very run down and tired for the last few weeks. He sends you to the clinic where they do one or two tests. Before you know what is happening they have rushed you up to the ward. They do some more tests and everyone runs around looking very worried.

Then the doctor comes in and tells you that you are very seriously ill and you will need to have a big operation tomorrow. He says you will be in for at least a week. Two days later another doctor comes to see you. He tells you that you have a very rare form of cancer. It is very advanced and the outlook is terrible.

Your whole world has fallen apart in an instant: all your hopes and dreams for the future have been dashed. It cannot really be true. It is hard to take in. Your plans for training, a job, a home of your own, maybe to get married and have children, and live to a ripe old age—all of these things have been crushed.

Your parents are beside themselves with worry and grief. What kind of a world is it where children die before their parents? It is like the whole natural order has been turned upside down.

Feeling suicidal

But AIDS can seem worse than any of this. Sometimes I ask a class at school what they would do if they went to give blood and a few days later a letter came asking them to reattend. When they go back, a man there tells them that their blood has tested positive for HIV.

Many people tell me they would commit suicide. They could not face the thought of everyone wondering how they had got it. How could they tell Dad? Could they tell him about being gay and having had sex with lots of other boys and men? Could they let on about parties at college that went on too late and too far; about messing around with drugs, or about other things he would frown on?

Many people do feel like committing suicide and some kill themselves just after finding out about AIDS or an early infection, which is why so much care and support is needed after someone has been told. A friend of mine who is a doctor was shocked one day last year to wake up in the morning and find that someone had parked his car at the bottom of his garden and had gassed himself with the exhaust. He had discharged himself against advice from the AIDS ward just a few hours previously. He could not face the thought of life with AIDS.

Throw him out

I remember one occasion when we had a couple round for dinner. The subject of AIDS came up as it often does because it is the whole of my work. Then the conversation turned to homosexuality and the ways different people develop as they grow up. I was shocked when the wife told us in no uncertain terms that if their five-year-old son was ever to develop signs of being homosexually inclined as a teenager, whether he remained celibate or not, she would throw him out of the house and have nothing more to do with him. No wonder many people with AIDS are careful who they tell. In most people's minds, to admit you have AIDS is the same thing as admitting you are a practising homosexual, although as we have seen this is often quite untrue.

Collecting the corpse

I went onto an AIDS ward one day and was disturbed to see an anxious young man who was obviously near to death, and dying on his own. I asked where his family were and whether they had been contacted. The answer was that he had been unable to bring himself to tell them what was happening and he did not want anyone else to do so. He was deteriorating fast. Possibly in the morning the ward would ring his mother 300 miles away, to come and collect the corpse of her son whom she thought was fit and well as a law student at London University.

When she came she would probably hardly recognise him. His body was a mere skeleton compared to how he had been seven months ago. His face was sunken and his skin was covered in an angry rash. His body bore the scars of a long hard fight against several infections. He had asked that the death certificate should only say 'pneumonia' because he wanted to save her the pain. If she had known the truth who would she ever be able to tell?

Living at home

I have just been on the telephone to someone with AIDS at home called Mark. He is being looked after by some of our volunteers who, together with our trained nurses and others provided by the NHS, are enabling him to fulfil his dying wish to stay at home. He has come to terms with what is happening, and is able to talk about it. Our team go in to do whatever he wants or needs. Last week it was making breakfast for him and his ailing mother most mornings, calling for the washing and ironing, helping with the shopping and delivering a special chair.

His mother lives a long distance away in a small town. She knows how harsh people are whenever they talk about AIDS up there. She knows that when she goes home she will never be able to talk about what has happened. She will say he died of cancer. If she told the truth she would never be able to lift her head high again. For her, learning about her son's homosexuality was a bit of a shock. She just used to think of him as a bachelor. Even now she doesn't fully understand, but he is her own flesh and blood, and she knows she cannot walk away.

The great cover up

One day, when he has died, she will go back home and nurse her grief alone. We have a home care programme in her area so we will visit her and maybe help her to talk to other mums or dads near her who have just been through the same thing. One of the reasons you think you don't know anyone who has died of AIDS is that it is all kept so quiet. Two senior politicians or even a member of the Royal Family could die of AIDS and you might never know.

Sometimes the anger is so fierce that it affects those who are doing the caring. A good friend of mine was told by her dad earlier this week that she was being cut off from the family. From now on it will be as if she did not exist. Her great crime was to fall in love with a man who some years previously had become infected and was now ill. For many months she cared for him, and after he had died, the final crime was to decide to carry on caring for those with AIDS.

A community nurse in London had recently had a long day. That night, in bed with her husband, she began to tell him about someone with AIDS who had been very ill and upset at home, and who she had spent some time with. 'Get out of this bed,' he shouted, 'and don't come back in here until you have stopped going there.'

You can begin to understand now why a senior teacher at a school for young children was petrified to find himself on the AIDS ward. Having AIDS was the least of his worries, nor was he afraid of dying. He was scared in case anyone from the school came to see him and it got back to the parents or the governors from the staff what was wrong with him. His whole reputation and career would be in tatters.

You can also understand a clergyman who was constantly afraid that one of his own parishioners who worked in the hospital would come up to the ward and recognise him. An increasing number of church leaders are becoming ill from AIDS, commonly because of gay lifestyles, or from being in the drug scene before a more recent conversion experience.

Getting the sack

People often lose their jobs when the boss finds out why they are ill. Sometimes you can lose your job for much less. A cinema projectionist was sacked recently and his appeal at the industrial tribunal was thrown out. They sacked him because he was known to be gay. Quite how a projectionist, shut up in a hot cubby hole showing films, could affect the cinema was not clear, but he lost his job nonetheless. Just think what would have happened to the poor man if someone had said he had AIDS.

A number of companies were asked what they would do if they found they were employing someone who had AIDS. Quite a few said they would sack the person straight away. Others said they would encourage the person to leave. Either way it was clear that in the future a lot of people with AIDS are going to find themselves on the dole, even though they may be perfectly well enough to work most of the time.

It is not just businesses that are severe. A solicitor was asked the other day to pack his case and go: 'We don't want that sort of thing here.'

Bust and dying

Every day the number of people with financial difficulties because of AIDS is growing. These days young people often use credit cards and take out loans for things like furniture or cars much more than older people. People are keen to give young people large mortgages because they know that young people are likely to be promoted over the years and their earning power will grow.

A pensioner who is dying because of AIDS does not have to work to live. A man who is nearing retirement may be able to take early retirement. Older people tend to own their houses, furniture and cars. But a young person who is suddenly having to take a £5,000 drop in salary can be very quickly in heavy debt. Recent changes in the DHSS benefit system have made things much more difficult, which is why our Team gives out so many grants.

Two weeks ago I went to have a medical—even doctors have to have them. With a wife and three young children to support I felt it was time I increased the amount of money they would receive if I was to die unexpectedly. Insurance companies are very jumpy when it comes to AIDS, and I wondered if they were going to make a fuss because I work for an AIDS charity, or because I look after people with AIDS as a doctor. In fact I was not asked to have a test. Many companies would like to be able to test all young people before agreeing to insure them. Because it would cause a public uproar they have decided on something just as drastic instead.

Paying out millions

They have simply decided to double or even treble the amount a young man or woman has to pay for life or medical insurance. They are doing it because they fear they will go bust unless they do it soon. They are expecting a great number of young people living in your area to die early, before they have paid many monthly premiums. The companies think they will be paying out millions of pounds to the relatives of a group of people who haven't put much in.

They are also afraid that sometimes they are being taken for a ride. Sometimes they notice a young man die just a year or two after taking out a massive life policy worth several hundred thousand pounds. The money is payable to another young man at the same address. They check through the records and find that the family doctor wrote that he had not seen this young man for years and was not under any treatment when the policy was taken out. Next they write to the hospital wondering if the man had AIDS.

The hospital will not tell them the cause of death. They suspect the man went for a test two years ago which came back positive. He knew that the hospital, which always sends results to the family doctor for every other illness, would not do so for AIDS. So when the insurance company wrote for a medical report to his family doctor it came back all clear, although the man was already ill and under treatment.

They cannot prove it of course, but some companies believe they may have been robbed of millions of pounds already by this route. Since they cannot test people, the only thing they can do is spread the cost around onto all young people who want cover.

For most large loans and for many kinds of mortgages, the person lending the money usually wants you to pay for some insurance in case you die before the loan has been repaid. In the case of an endowment mortgage, someone with AIDS cannot get one without lying, which as we have seen can be the only option for someone who wants to get life cover.

Nowhere to live

In addition to all the harsh attitudes we have seen—the employment difficulties, problems with insurance and mortgages—there is yet another big problem for someone when it gets around he has AIDS: housing.

Many young people are very mobile. They have chosen not to settle down yet, are often not in a position to buy their own home or do not want to wait years in one place to get a council flat. Often they end up in bedsits or small expensive flats owned by private landlords. It frequently happens that the landlord objects if he discovers one of his tenants has AIDS. Maybe he is afraid the rest of the people will move out when they get to hear, or maybe he has harsh feelings like some of the others we have seen. Either way, it is quite common for someone to come out of hospital after just being told they have AIDS, to discover their belongings have been turfed out and the locks have been changed.

Sometimes the culprit is the person they have been living with. I know of one occasion where someone found the locks changed by a former lover, and another where the former lover had cleaned the flat out leaving nothing, not even a chair, a lamp, a table or a bed to sleep on. We were able to buy this man a new bed immediately, but a whole home takes time to rebuild.

Wandering the streets

The number of people who have become homeless because of AIDS is growing each week and is becoming a major problem in London. Various agencies are trying to locate people who would be willing to have someone with AIDS live with them for a while until suitable accommodation can be found.

The usual council response is to put people in bed and breakfast accommodation. This can be very hard on someone who is dying as they are thrown out by 10 o'clock every morning and have to wander the streets in all weathers until the evening. Also these places often have a lot of stairs which people with AIDS can find hard or impossible to climb.

Twice now a man's house in London has been set on fire by neighbours because they thought the person concerned might possibly be infected. Fortunately on both occasions he was out and no one else was harmed.

Who can I trust?

In all of this you can see that someone with AIDS has most of the things to cope with that someone with cancer has, as well as the extra tragedy of having a terminal disease so young—I speak as a doctor with experience of both diseases. But the worst thing by far is the response of the people around you. Will the next person I meet feel sorry for me (which I hate) or want to see me dead and tell me it's all my own fault? Who is my friend and who is my enemy? If I tell my friend about my illness, will it be kept a secret, or how many days will it take before my friend has told someone else?

No wonder suicide is seen as a better option by some.

Am I infected too?

There is yet another more sinister problem. With cancer, if you are looking after your spouse or partner until he or she dies, it is normal to worry sometimes that you will die of the same illness. Doctors and nurses are the same. People often imagine they have the same illnesses as the people they are with. Sometimes after a loved one has died, a widow may turn up at her doctor's with identical aches and pains. These are quite real but are a part of grieving, not a result usually of physical illness.

But with AIDS there is a terrible thought at the back of a lover's mind: if we have often had sex together, then there is a big risk I could be about to develop AIDS too. People find themselves having a good look each day for the blue marks of Kaposi's sarcoma skin cancer, or waking at night afraid. It is not a fear that is easy to remove. Our volunteers have been going into the home of someone who has AIDS. His lover was at work, but now we have two sick people in the same home. Each is watching the other die. This causes immense distress, even more awful because each can somehow blame himself for the other being ill.

Friends coming in may also have already lost a number of other close friends from AIDS. In San

Francisco many of the people I met had already lost between ten and twenty of their friends. In London the figures are sometimes between five and ten. The accumulated shock, grief and anguish can mean that people run out of energy and inner resources.

Softening people's attitudes

AIDS is a horrible disease to have, and to cope with it requires an unusual amount of courage and strength. You have to learn to live with constant rejection, isolation and loneliness. Support groups such as Body Positive, the Buddies, helplines, the Lighthouse and other agencies have all had an important part to play in ensuring that people with AIDS have somewhere to turn. But there is still a lot to be done, and with the numbers doubling each year we have to move fast or we shall be overtaken. Many of the problems we have seen could be removed by softening people's attitudes, which is the subject of the next chapter.

7
What Do You Think?

1. Whose fault is it?

I want now to look at sex and AIDS, and some of the ways people think about them. For some reason everyone seems to want to point the finger when it comes to AIDS. They begin when arguing about where AIDS first came from. The true answer is that no one knows, although we are sure that HIV was around in several parts of the world in the 1960s. It is similar to common viruses in animals and has probably been around in some shape or form for centuries. Because many scientists think it could originally have come from animals in Africa, people immediately think Africa is in some way to blame. This is stupid. Whatever the facts show in the future, the disease had to start somewhere and it is no one's fault where it first came from.

'They should have known better'

The other big area where people seem to point fingers is where particular groups or individuals are infected. Some people say it is their own fault. Depending on how far they take it, you get the impression that some actually believe that anyone who has a certain lifestyle deserves an automatic death sentence.

Some people say those infected should have known better, but they forget that most of those dying now were infected before many people had even heard of AIDS, let alone understood how it was spread.

Some people say that anyone, say, with a gay lifestyle or a drug habit should realise that these are wrong and should expect the consequences. This can make those infected feel even more guilty and blame themselves too. They also can often feel very guilty about people they may have infected without realising.

Pointing the finger is the easy way out

Many illnesses are caused by lifestyles that some would question: should we have any sympathy for a man who has smoked fifty cigarettes a day for the last forty years and now has terrible bronchitis or lung cancer? What about a young girl who falls downstairs and breaks her leg at a party because she has had too much to drink?

At the end of the day it is easier to blame people and have nothing to do with them. It is a neat and tidy way of making it someone else's problem. You don't have to feel guilty about not getting involved because in your own mind you have made everyone else guilty. It is the same mentality as the man who says you should not help the starving in Africa because it is all their own fault for having such large families (even though this is rubbish because Africa has the capacity to produce more than enough food for millions more people).

Harsh churches

Because I am a church leader as well as a doctor looking after people with AIDS, people often ask me what I think about AIDS as a Christian. They hear different things. Some people say AIDS is the wrath or judgement of God on homosexuals, and others say it is nothing of the sort. Some leaders have even said Christian people should have nothing to do with AIDS and others are saying that every Christian should make some sort of response. A lot of opinions, but what should we think about it all?

A personal view

AIDS is not the wrath of God on the gay community: it never was. About seven years ago the only people we knew who were infected with HIV were, as you know, gay men. Clergymen all over the world then began tub-thumping sermons warning that it was the wrath of God against gay people and was an expression of his anger about gay lifestyles.

Egg on their faces

Some of these people are still saying the same things—the ones who never read newspapers and are seven years out of date. Others now have egg on their faces and want to hide in embarrassment.

As we have seen, AIDS is not a gay plague. It never was a gay plague, and most of the people in the world who are infected are infected because of sex between a man and a woman. I am convinced that in this country, drugs and sex between men and women will soon overtake homosexual sex as the main cause of new infections. In fact it may well have done so already.

Lesbians are exempt

It always was a rather stupid thing to say anyway. After all, lesbians (homosexual women) are the only group in our society, other than monks or nuns, in whom AIDS is almost unknown. It is very hard indeed for a lesbian to pass on the infection to another woman she has sex with. God's judgement is remarkably selective if we are to believe these leaders. This would mean that God hates sex between two men, next he hates sex between a man and a woman outside marriage, but he doesn't really mind sex between two women. This is clearly absurd.

As a friend of mine said recently, if this is a blast from God's shotgun, he has a pretty poor aim! What about the tens of thousands of young children infected in Africa as a result of medical treatments?

If, as some have suggested, it turns out that medical treatments with infected equipment or blood have in fact caused more deaths in Africa than anything, what do we say then? God's wrath on those who are ill and need medical care?

Nothing new

People get very excited over AIDS. They think that AIDS is something quite new, and as strange as a thunderbold from heaven. They need to talk to some older people with longer memories and read the history books. As we have seen, AIDS is just another in a long series of diseases which can be spread by sex. These things have been around for centuries, and AIDS may well have been around in some shape or form for hundreds of years.

Was syphilis the wrath of God? It spread as a plague starting several hundred years ago. There was no cure. It made people sterile and caused them to have all kinds of strange illnesses over many years. It attacked the heart, blood vessels, kidneys, liver, and finally rotted the brain. We used to call the final stages 'paralysis of the insane'. Not a nice way to die.

When penicillin was discovered, did God suddenly decide that he didn't mind and was going to allow the plague to stop? If AIDS is the judgement of God then syphilis is too.

The Bible says we can enjoy most things, but too much can be bad for us. That is why getting drunk is described as a bad thing to do. So, is the plague of people dying from too much drink, from liver failure and other things, God's wrath as well?

Just another disease

As a doctor I know that AIDS is just a disease. It is caused by a virus common in animals which has been around almost certainly for a long time. Sex is an easy way for a lazy germ to travel and a great number of germs find it convenient to get around this way. When we have a cure for AIDS there will doubtless be a whole string of new germs that appear on the scene being spread by sex.

So AIDS certainly is not a gay plague, and I do not think it was sent by an angel as a thunderbolt from God to shake us all up.

2. Cause and effect

Common sense

You get out of life what you put into it, or as Jesus said, 'you reap what you sow.' This is a personal view as a Christian who takes what the Bible says seriously. I don't ask you to agree with it or like what I say, but it is, I think, a common-sense view.

Any doctor knows that the majority of the illnesses he sees could probably be avoided or reduced if people lived differently. Heart disease is becoming less common in some countries now, because people are more health conscious. They watch their weight and take exercise. Smoking is also on the decline— just as well since nicotine is one of the most addictive drugs known to science. You get a shot of nicotine every time a cigarette burns and you inhale the greasy smoke. Smoking kills around 120,000 people a year in the UK alone. Most of these people who are dying now first became nicotine addicts before they left school.

Health education

The whole of health education is showing people cause and effect: if you smoke you damage your lungs. If you drive when you are stoned out of your brains you are likely to drive off the road and kill someone. If you get drunk you have a hangover. If you inject using a bloody needle you can get hepatitis or develop AIDS.

Cause and effect is the most important lesson we have to learn as children. My daughter shut her fingers in a door recently and had to be taken to hospital. Her thumb was a mess, but it is perfectly healed now. I hope she has learnt that you must not put your fingers in the cracks of doors because the door can close and you can get badly hurt. If she doesn't learn she will be a real danger to herself.

Learning the hard way

Because I love my daughter I will try to save her the pain of having to learn the hard way. If she jumps on top of her sister's top bunk I tell her off because I am afraid that one day she will lose her balance and fall. She probably won't do it again after falling, but I would rather she didn't fall in the first place. When you were young your parents probably told you a hundred times a day to come away from something or to put something down. Most of the time your own safety was the issue. Your mother probably then explained to you, for example, that an oven is extremely hot and if you touch it with your fingers you will burn yourself badly.

None of us is very good at listening at first. Usually there are one or two near disasters: 'I told you so. That was naughty. Now when I tell you next time, you do exactly what I say.' And then we learn.

Strange ideas

People have really strange ideas about God sometimes. They think of him as some great tyrant or bully or some distant figure they can't relate to at all. The Bible says that God is a loving Father, a million times better than your human dad. Because he loves us, he looks on us as his children. He cares about each person as if that person is the only person in the whole world.

Because he cares for us that much he wants to help us and to protect us from our own mistakes. But he respects you as a person and he will never dominate your life. He is always there ready and waiting to help you, but you must ask. He will never impose himself. Nor will he ever go away. You can turn your back on him for years, but he is always there ready and waiting with open arms. There is nothing that you can do that can put you outside his love for you, although you can remain distanced from him with consequences both here and in the next life.

True love means no strings attached

Jesus told the story of the prodigal son who left homewith loads of money from his dad. He basically fell out with his dad and wanted to go off to a big town and do his own thing. He found living on his own was terrible. He had a really hard time. He blew all the money on trying to live it up and then found himself having to work for a pittance in order to eat. He kept wondering if his dad would accept him back again.

After a while he was so fed up he reckoned that even if his dad wouldn't accept him back as a member of the family he would prefer to go home on any terms. When he was almost home he got nervous, but his dad saw him coming from a distance and rushed out to meet him. The son felt ashamed and wouldn't even look up, but his father flung his arms around him and swept him into the house, cancelled all his arrangements and threw a great coming home party, much to the disgust of a certain other member of the family.

Jesus told the story to show us that God's love never goes cold or goes away, just because we go cold or go away from God.

Design for living

I am telling you this because unless you can begin to understand how much the Bible says God loves you, you will never really understand why the Bible is so keen on telling you how to avoid the pain of your own mistakes, and how to live a happy, full and satisfying life.

The Bible is full of examples of cause and effect. In fact you could say it is one of the main things the

Bible talks about: 'If you do this, such and such is likely to happen.'

It contains an enormous amount of health information. Much of it was written many thousands of years ago when the writers could not possibly have known about germs and how disease was spread.

The Bible contains for me a brilliant guide to healthy living. We often see it as full of negative commands: don't do this and don't do that. My children can also see me as very negative if they don't realise that what I say is actually for their benefit, safety and happiness. It would be a strange dad who constantly let his children put their lives at risk without doing something about it. And it would be a strange God who made a world full of people and just let them get on with it without even giving them some help and advice when they were looking for it.

How to wreck your life

The Bible basically says that if you want to wreck your life then a really good way to do it is to wreck your relationships with people—not just any people, but the people you are close to, your closest friends, your partner, or your family.

And if you want to mess up your close relationships and family completely, then a good way to do it is to have sex with a person or people you are not married to.

If a father wants to guarantee that he has no relationship with his daughter, so much so that maybe she isn't willing to even call him dad any more, then the quickest way to do it is to seduce her and have sex with her, preferably at a young age and over a number of years.

How to be lonely and alone in later life

Tens of thousands of thirty-five to forty-five-year-olds are having a terrible shock. They grew up deciding that marriage was out and it was better just to live together. After three or four relationships they have found themselves on their own yet again. For women the chances now of ever settling down and having a family are vanishing fast.

Men can also suddenly find that the long party over the years has come to an end. They are no longer as attractive and dynamic as they were. They have lots of memories, but no life-long commitment, and no real ideas about how to find one, because most of the women who were into such things settled down with other men long ago.

How to wreck your marriage

If a man wants to destroy his marriage completely overnight, then the quickest way to do it is to cheat on his wife by having an affair, say, with her best friend. He will probably lose his children and the respect of his other friends at the same time. Sometimes, those of us who pick up the pieces find it unbelievable that people can't see things which are staring them in the face. They still go on to make stupid decisions that anyone watching with any sense at all can see will end in disaster.

If as a young person you want to make it more likely that your future marriage will fall to bits within five years, then a really effective way is to try to get into bed with everyone you can while you can. Patterns don't change because of ten minutes in a registry office. If you program your brain and your body to react in a particular way, then it can be really hard suddenly to become the perfect faithful husband.

Sex before marriage means that your partner in marriage is under a lot of pressure: 'Jacky used to be a lot better in bed. She could really get me going,' or, 'Every time we make love I keep thinking how Bill used to hold me...he used to do it like this.'

Private place

I'm glad that the only person I have ever made love to is my wife. I am glad too that we never made love before we got married. For us it was an expression of total commitment to each other. Right up until the wedding day there was the opportunity to call it off. Many engagements do not result in marriage, and some engagements should never have gone on into what turned out to be very unhappy marriages. People need to know what makes a happy marriage, and how they can be reasonably sure they are about to marry the right person.

For my wife and me, our whole language of love has been built up with each other. It is ours alone. It is our secret. It is a private place exclusive to us. No one else can intrude into that special place. It is a sign every time we come together of our exclusive commitment and unity.

The Bible says that when a man and a woman come together they become, in a sense, 'one flesh'.

Sex is a mystery, not just a sensation. People—especially girls or women—I have spoken to who tried sex out of curiosity have often been disappointed. They told everyone it was wonderful, but were really left wondering what all the fuss was about.

3. A good sex life

Sex is more than a physical act. In medicine I am glad that we are at last moving away from looking at people like cars or other machines, where you just replace or repair bits. People are people. Whole person medicine is where we recognise that you are more than a kidney stone or an appendix: you are you, you have personal needs, feelings, hopes and fears which go to make up what you are and are actually far more important than the illness. The illness is just a nuisance because it is preventing you from being you.

Glossy magazines have pushed sex as some kind of wonder drug. You get the impression that sex once a day keeps the problems or the doctor away. If you are not having sex regularly then they lead you to believe you are underdeveloped, frigid, impotent, or just plain stupid. But I don't see a high level of deep satisfaction and fulfilment. Agony columns are full of people who are obsessed by poor sexual performance and lack of enjoyment that they dare not tell anyone about so they write instead.

Sex is a language

Sex is not a performance; it is possibly the deepest form of communication and expression known to human beings. But like any language, if there is nothing to communicate then it is empty and hollow.

When I was at college I remember vividly a couple coming into my room. They had slept together a couple of times over the previous weeks—the first time for both of them—and had really regretted it. They were not Christians and it was nothing to do with morality. They had come to realise that sex is not instant; that it takes a while for two people to build up their own language of love, to discover how to give each other the greatest pleasure, and that they had wandered into this area too soon.

I am glad that when I make love to my wife I can tell her that I have never made love to anyone else. She owns my body and I belong to her. There is a real strength in that. And if difficult times come—and they can come in any relationship, albeit not for long—then the barrier to having sex with another woman is enormously greater than if I were just to drift back to an old pattern of 'sleeping around'.

Making sure you are compatible

People say you should have sex together before you get married to find out whether you are compatible or not. People who say this obviously don't know the first thing about the facts of life. If they did they would know that there is no such thing as a man too big for a woman or a woman too big for a man.

Unless the man has a penis thicker than a baby's head the woman will be able to accommodate him—after all, where a man goes in a baby has to come out! Boys are often obsessed with the size of their equipment. Too small or too big? When a woman is aroused, all the parts inside and outside begin to change shape so that even a man not particularly well endowed will have a snug fit. We have been well designed!

Incredibly rarely a doctor may see a couple who are unable to have sex because of a slight abnormality; for example, a thin layer of skin completely closing off the woman just inside her. Such a woman does not produce blood when she menstruates, so the reason is usually clear and easily dealt with. But apart from rarities like that, incompatibility does not exist. Impotence in a man can be very distressing, but the biggest cause by far is nerves about whether he will perform all right or not, and a man is much more likely to be afraid if he is on some kind of pre-marriage trial. Marriage gives a couple time, space and security in which to relax.

Secret of a good sex life

However, there is no such thing as an instantly compatible couple. Every person is different and every couple is totally unique. Things that one person may find very pleasurable, another may find a complete turn-off. Good love-making takes time, privacy, care, understanding and good communication. Maybe that is why many couples find their love-making gets better and better as they learn more and more about each other. The most basic requirement, however, is a good warm relationship where, especially for the woman, both partners can really give of themselves in an atmosphere of total security. Only when you are totally secure are you fully free.

When you split sex from the whole-person experience, you are doomed to only part fulfilment. This leads to a steadily worsening spiral, looking always for the ultimate in sexual release. The next person, or this new way of doing it, may yet be better than before.

How to wreck good sex

Girls usually realise these things long before the men they go out with do. Most girls need no persuading about the advantages of being in a secure loving relationship. In fact one of the main reasons why (against their better judgement) some are willing finally to sleep with boyfriends is the hope that through offering them sex they will be able to attract their boyfriends into a long-term relationship.

Unfortunately in my experience it usually works the other way. A girl a man used to respect, almost revere, he now despises as cheap and worthless, like all the rest. A woman's greatest asset is her mystery, and the moment she has sex with her boyfriend she is in danger of losing it. The Bible says that when a man has slept with a woman, he 'knows' her. There is a sense in which everything has been uncovered.

4. Sex and the church

Confusion in the church

There is confusion in some parts of the church over just about everything at the moment. It seems you can have a bishop who rejects Jesus as the Son of God, rejects the virgin birth, thinks that the resurrection never really happened and that the Bible is not really to be believed. Once you have a group of people who have decided to reject major parts of the Bible, along with many of the historic teachings of the church, you have major problems. After all, any man's opinion is then as valid as anyone else's. You can end up with as many different religions as there are people.

As an atheist friend of mine said recently, if you want to join the club you must reckon to obey the rules. The trouble here is that it seems some people think they can rewrite the basis of the club's existence, and therefore regard rules they don't like as invalid, and ignore them.

You might forgive existing club members of thinking that these 'radicals' are not radical at all. They have just invented a brand new club of their own.

Daring to be honest

If I am going to be honest and read the Bible carefully to understand what the *whole* of it says about life, not just a sentence or two, then I am going to have to be very careful. You can easily read bits of phrases here and there and string them out to say just about whatever you want them to. The overall meaning is vitally important.

This is my own conclusion about what the Bible says about sex and sexuality. You need to read the Bible for yourself. I read the entire Bible through three times in as many years, often making detailed notes and using reference books to make sure I really understood what was being said. What I am going to say now is in the light of those readings.

As I see it, the Bible teaches right from the start that God made man and woman in his own image. His intention is that a man should marry a woman, and that sex is to be a wonderful gift, a mystery uniting a man and woman who have committed themselves to each other in this way for life.

Family life

Out of that kaleidoscope of rich physical love are to come children who grow up in a secure loving family, with grannies and grandpas, aunts and uncles, nephews and nieces, and single people included in family life if they want.

Marriage is the basic foundation stone. Therefore it is no surprise to the Christian to find that where marriages break down; where there is violence in the home; where spouses cheat on each other and stop caring; that children often grow up with deep scars, insecure and unsure of themselves. A lot of vandalism, alcohol problems, drug problems and other situations can be traced to unhappy homes of the young people concerned.

The Bible, by encouraging everything that supports a good stable marriage, speaks out against anything that undermines marriage as the rock on which society is built. We live in an era which has regarded marriage largely as an irrelevance. To be married is not chic. Look at the adverts on the television tonight. How many women of whatever ages, especially in shots of couples, are wearing a wedding ring—or even an engagement ring?

Careers have encouraged women to put off having children for ten years or more. The tragedy is, that when they finally want them they often find their peak of fertility has passed, getting pregnant is difficult and the risks of having a baby with an abnormality are increased. In medicine, anyone having a first child over the age of thirty is regarded as an elderly mum because doctors recognise that the female body was not really designed for such a late first pregnancy.

Sex designed for marriage

Because the Bible is for marriage, and against what discourages marriage, the Bible is for keeping sexual union as the exclusive activity of those who are married. Before the pill some twenty years ago, sex meant babies who needed Mum and Dad—permanently. Any family doctor will tell you that casual relationships are bad for children and bad for family life. Jesus made it absolutely clear that he agreed with the established teaching, which was that sex outside marriage was wrong. In fact he went further, to say that even to have a fantasy about sex outside marriage was also wrong.

I am not asking you to agree with this. All I am asking you to do is to be honest with yourself and at least admit that this is what the Bible says. It is in fact the teaching that has always been given by the church, although there have always been small groups who have written their own rulebooks, and sometimes in the process found themselves outside the church as a result. This teaching is not the teaching of one denomination, but of the whole of the Christian church since the time of Jesus, whether Catholic, Eastern Orthodox, Anglican, Methodist, Baptist, or whatever. In fact it is one of the few things on which Christians over the centuries have always been united.

Stretching the limits

Some people have tried to make out there is a special case for those who have attraction to others of the same sex. The Bible teaches that people can be sexually aroused in a great number of different situations. It is very explicit. The Bible describes men having sex with men, adults having sex with children, men having sex with their mothers, people having sex with animals, orgies, prostitution and many other things. Homosexual sex is mentioned directly in a number of places in the Bible—always as something beyond what is allowed.

However, the Bible also describes very close, warm, intense, loving relationships between people of the same sex—David and Jonathan for example.

David and Jonathan could share as much of their lives together as they liked, but they could not indulge in homosexual activity.

Fashionable faith

People say it is very unfair. It is also hard for a woman who finds that the only man she has ever loved is married to another woman. A man who has never been able to find the right person to marry is also confronted with a choice: a lifetime of celibacy, or an illicit sexual union? For women, celibacy has always been a common option. Whenever war killed many future husbands, unmarried women were left. This happened at the end of the first world war which is one of the reasons why we have so many elderly single women today.

We think in this sex-dominated age that to expect a man not to express his sexuality by having sex with another person is somehow against the laws of nature and is wrong. It is no different than for a woman, except that a man's urges are often far stronger. The Christian faith does not change every time fashions change. In the next century people will look with some amusement at the adolescent 1980s with its obsession with sex, and the domination of sex diseases.

5. Caring is not the same as agreeing

You may not agree. I am not asking you to agree, but only to see what I have written as a view which is as valid as yours. We can agree to disagree, and still respect each other as people, respect each other for our integrity, honesty and openness, and care about each other.

Recently I was talking to a journalist from the BBC who said she was shocked that certain groups of Christians had given support to an AIDS hospice. She had expected groups who supported gay priests in the church and were a part of the gay community would be at the forefront, but that others who had a more traditional view would want nothing to do with helping people with AIDS—except perhaps to abuse their position by moralising or preaching to people on their deathbeds.

Practical care

I told her she had confused agreeing with caring. They have never been the same thing in medicine. If, as a doctor, I only looked after people who voted for the same party, who held the same faith, who worshipped in the same kind of church, who never did anything I personally could not approve of, I think I should be struck off the medical register right away. Doctors and nurses are expected to give good compassionate care to all who need it and for all illnesses, regardless of how people come to be ill. The same is true for all those involved in the so-called caring professions.

San Francisco

When I went to the Shanti project in San Francisco I was impressed by the great love and care being given by members of the gay community to people who were ill with AIDS. I was welcomed by one of the directors, who told me she had once been married and had had several children before 'coming out' as a lesbian. I told her I felt unsure of myself. Here I was a 'straight' man in an almost totally gay environment. To make matters worse, as a Christian I could not with integrity say that I thought gay lifestyles were wonderful, and if I was honest I would have to say my own understanding of the Bible was that such activity, like any other sexual union outside marriage, was not on for a Christian.

I told her I was beginning to understand just a little about what it must be like to be gay; working in a mainly heterosexual environment, wondering how people would react if they knew. How would people in Shanti react if they knew about me? Would they reject me? Was there room for a straight Christian who wanted to be involved with the terrible suffering he had seen and wanted to help?

She said words I will never forget: 'Honey,' she said, taking my hand, 'I am a member of the gay community myself. I am not a Christian, but I think some people are crazy with the risks they are taking. I tell them off for being so stupid. I think some of the things they are doing are wrong...but I love them, cry with them, weep over them, pin their photos to the wall when they have gone. You don't have to agree in order to care. Welcome!'

Room to care

For me it was like a ray of light had just shone in. So many people have excluded themselves from the care of those with AIDS because they feel that they have to be a paid up member of the gay community to be involved. People I know have come away from training courses run by some organisations, feeling that because they were unable to put hand on heart and say gay lifestyles are liberating and wonderful maybe they had no role in AIDS care.

AIDS is such a big problem that we urgently need to broaden the support base available to people who have it. This is especially true now we are finding a smaller and smaller proportion of new infections are happening in the gay community. We are also finding that many members of the gay community who have been at the forefront of helping those infected or with AIDS, are themselves now ill, or dying, or are worn out by so many deaths of close friends. People with haemophilia, or a drug habit, mothers with children and other heterosexual men and women also have needs which have to be met.

As a church leader I have to ask whether the church is ready to make the kind of response that people with AIDS need it to make. Are *you* ready?

8

Where Are You Going?

If we are going to look after people who are dying, then we need to have come to terms ourselves with what we think about death.

Shaken by the violence

It takes a lot of bottle to look death in the eye and keep on looking. The first time it happened to me I was still at school. I was walking along a busy street and saw a bus collide with a woman on a pedestrian crossing. She was smashed to the ground in an instant. There she was lying in the road bleeding and gasping for breath. We all gathered round. I had never done first aid at school and didn't know what to do. Someone was holding her head. The driver had got out of his cab shocked, and someone had run off to get an ambulance. As I watched from a distance she suddenly vomited, choked, went rapidly blue and died.

I went home shaken at the violence of what had happened. You can see 100 things like that on the television, but when you see it close up it becomes real. What shocked me even more was to discover later that she had died because she was lying on her back and had drowned in her own vomit.

My second experience of death was after I had just left school. It was a dark wet night and I was sitting on the bottom deck at the front of a double-decker bus with an open rear. As it sped along the edge of the common on the black greasy road, I was surprised by the crash of loose change on the deck. I turned round and saw nothing, and then to my horror noticed through the back window the bus conductor lying in the road. He had been coming down the stairs and slipped, hitting his head on the deck and bouncing out onto the tarmac.

I rushed to the bell and rang it for what seemed like an eternity before the heavy bus pulled to a halt. I leapt out and raced back. A queue of cars had already stopped. A nurse got out and gave some assistance, but he later died of his massively fractured skull.

Fear of the unknown

In our culture we don't like to talk about death. We deny death exists. By the way some people talk, you would think they are immortal. Children are often kept well away from funerals, usually because adults are embarrassed to cry in front of them. In the last century death was never far away, but now with modern medicine and improved living conditions it catches us by surprise.

It is this fear of death, the fear of the unknown, that is the main reason why AIDS is so scary. People often ask me how I can bear to spend my life looking after people who are dying—it used to be cancer, but now it's AIDS. I tell them that the reason is because I know where I'm going.

When I had just qualified as a doctor, one of the first patients I had was a retired woman who was dying of cancer. I remember sitting on her bed one afternoon and she took my hand. 'You'll remember me when I've gone, won't you,' she said. I nodded and she went on: 'You know where you're going, don't you. You believe?' I had never said anything to her about faith. I do not carry a label, or a symbol, or a Bible, but she had picked something up. She had sensed that I was at peace with her dying. She could see that I was not afraid and that I was not going to abandon her because hope of her cure had abandoned me.

It is only as we get older that we get screwed up about dying. Young children are very matter of fact. Children who are dying usually treat it as a part of normal conversation, and are then very surprised to find out that all the adults cannot cope. They then quickly learn to shut up so as not to upset the family and the nursing staff.

I think some of the fears I used to have stemmed from some of the things I had been told as a child: 'He would have swallowed his dentures so we had to take them out' (how anyone could swallow a complete set of false teeth was beyond me, but made me think that something violent happened after the end). I was also told that after people died it was like the floodgates opened: waterworks and bowels emptied all over the bed.

You can imagine how relieved I was as a medical student to discover that these things do not happen: death, when managed properly, is almost always a very peaceful and dignified thing. Often the relative sitting in the room is not even sure if the person has died or not; he or she just appears to be sleeping.

Death is a mystery

If ever you have had the privilege of sitting with someone who is dying at the moment of death, you will have experienced a mystery. Here is a woman bounded by place and time. You are sitting there holding her hand. She is breathing quietly. Most of the time she is asleep, but occasionally she opens her eyes or says a word. She is not in any pain, she is not doped and she knows exactly what is happening. She is not afraid and is at peace.

As you are sitting there you notice that her breathing has become more laboured, and she seems sleepier. Over what seems like hours, but is in fact a few minutes, the breathing changes again. The nurse comes in and says her pulse is very weak and rapid now. There are small beads of sweat on her brow.

Gradually the breathing seems to fade away, and is gone. You wonder if she has died. After a few minutes you get a shock when she suddenly takes another deep breath before all is quiet again. In a while you realise she has gone.

A dead body is still alive

Nearly all the cells in her body are still alive. Her kidneys will be useful to someone if removed in the next half an hour. Her brain cells are too badly damaged to live for long, but her skin will still be alive in a week. The cornea (the clear bit of the eye), if removed by late tomorrow, will give a child sight, and her heart may still have cells within it which are beating. Her gut is still contracting and the stomach is still digesting food. All the proteins in her body are there, the bone marrow is still producing new blood cells. So what has happened?

At the end of the day it is a mystery. I always say that the nearest an atheist ever gets to a religious experience is his own death, and death heightens spiritual awareness in every way. It is a brave man who has just watched this mystery, or conversely just watched the birth of a child, who can walk away still as convinced that there is no God.

Four reactions to dying

When you know you are dying, four things start to happen. The first is that your priorities change. What is the point in carrying on with your course when the doctors have told you that you will probably be dead by Christmas? The second thing it does is alter your relationships. You find your best friend can't cope and hasn't visited you once in hospital, whereas someone in the same year who you never thought much of has been a real support and nothing is ever too much trouble. Sometimes it takes a terminal diagnosis for some people to really work out who they are, and who is important to them.

It can be a time of great regrets and some people find themselves looking back and wondering how they would have done things differently if they had known life was going to be so short.

Finally, people find they are looking forward. Most people I talk to are not so much afraid of death as afraid of dying: they are afraid of becoming incontinent, of losing control, of becoming a burden, of being totally dependent, afraid of pain, afraid of suffocating to death, afraid of losing the ability to think, move or remember.

And then there is another dimension: is there really no more to life than life? Is there really no more to me as a person than the molecules that go to make up my body? When I die, will that be the end, or is there another kind of existence after this one?

Deathbed conversion

These and many other questions often cause people to search. They go to mediums, spiritualists and any other agency that will reassure them that there is in fact life beyond the grave.

Deathbed conversion is very common and very real. The thief on the cross turned to Christ in the act of dying. I remember a man with lung cancer who came into St Joseph's Hospice while I was working there. He looked at the nuns and said: 'I'm an atheist. Do I have to be catholic to be here?'

We explained that people of all faiths, and none, were equally welcome. I don't think anyone spoke to him about any matter regarding personal faith or beliefs, until some two weeks later he suddenly raised the matter again and asked to see a priest. He had undergone a profound turnaround as he approached the end.

More to life than life

As a Christian I believe that there is a life after this one, and that death is merely a gateway from this world, limited by space and time, to another dimension. Jesus taught quite clearly that when this life is over, each of us will have to give an account of what we have done with our lives.

Jesus also showed us that no one is perfect and in ourselves none of us can please God. None of us is perfect enough to enter his presence and survive. The good news is that God has bridged that huge chasm between us and him by sending Jesus. The things we have done wrong have eternal consequences. We are responsible, and the penalty for what we have done is death and extinction.

But God sent Jesus to receive the punishment that should have been ours. By dying for us, Jesus set us free from the effects of our own wrong-doing. Through Jesus, for those who accept him and follow him, God has chosen to forgive us completely and to wipe the record completely clean. Through Jesus we can call on the unreachable, unknowable, unfathomable God as our Father.

For those who believe, the moment of death is a glorious change from being only partly aware of God and his love, to being fully and completely in his presence. For someone who never knew God and hated the things of God, the Bible teaches us that life after death will be an unpleasant, uncomfortable disappointment.

Practical care for people

This teaching about what happens after death, which has always been a central part of the church, immediately raises a question in many people's minds, especially when they read that many churches are becoming involved in providing practical care for people with AIDS at home. If Christians believe some people may find themselves separated from God after death, then they will surely want to get at every person they meet who is dying and preach the gospel?

I was talking to a prominent member of an AIDS organisation recently who also incidentally has AIDS himself. He is a convert to Buddhism and freely admitted with a smile that when he was with people who had AIDS all he really wanted to do was tell them about his faith, but he knew he could not.

What do you want?

If someone with AIDS asks to see a chaplain, he is asking for spiritual help. If all the chaplain is interested in doing is visiting him at home to do the ironing and washing up, you can imagine he might well feel let down. However, if someone with AIDS has asked for someone to help with the washing up and ironing and all the person seems to want to do is talk religion, you can imagine the person might well have good cause to feel annoyed.

It is a real privilege to be allowed to be with someone who is approaching the end of his or her life. It is a very special time, as all who have been involved will know. People are rightly very sensitive to others rushing in insensitively to someone who may be too weak to say 'no' or 'please go away'. Often it is only afterwards that the upset comes out and the person who is ill pleads for a certain helper never to come in again. Behind the polite face there can be real anguish which is often not expressed at the time. If you are vulnerable you think twice before antagonising someone on whom your life could depend.

Helpful or dreadful

If a doctor at a clinic asks a volunteer agency for a night sitter, he expects a night sitter, not a chaplain. If it gets back that a particular night sitter spent all night (it may not be true, but only a tiny part true) trying to convert his patient, the doctor may well feel justifiably angry. As far as he is concerned, the night-sitting service is completely useless.

It is not a service to him as a doctor because he would be extremely worried about asking someone else to go in from that group again. It is not a service for the patient because what the patient wanted was good company and a helping hand, and he got a preacher. The doctor comes to the conclusion that the night-sitting service is only interested in serving the local vicar or minister by trying to convert people. If that is the case, he as a doctor will campaign to make sure everyone knows about these dreadful people.

Guest and servant

There is a right time and a right place for everything. If you are making someone a meal and because he has noticed that you are always there, you never complain, you accept him as a person, you are happy to look after him even though he senses you do not share his views on lifestyle, because of all these things and because he knows you go to church he asks you about your faith, that is a completely different matter.

He is driving the conversation, and it would be stupid and unfriendly not to answer his questions. You might find that in the context of his own searchings he finds it reassuring to have someone around like you who has a faith. You might even find that he asks you to pray for him—it is surprising how often an atheist has faith in the prayers of someone else! But in everything, your attitude must be that of a servant: how can I be of most help today? Remember also that you are always there as a guest to assist, and never to take over.

Schools education

The same principles apply in schools education. Schools work is a very sensitive area where governors, parent/teacher associations, local authorities, government, teachers and, of course, pupils, all have strong views on how sex education and AIDS issues should be taught. People are afraid that activists will use the AIDS crisis to promote homosexuality in schools or to promote extreme moral views and harsh attitudes.

A schools educator is there at the invitation of the teacher to be a servant to the school, as a guest in the classroom. Topics to be covered, methods and general approach should all be agreed beforehand.

Working in schools is a privilege and should not be a platform for promotion of personal views or beliefs. However, if in the context of religious education or likeskill classes an educator is asked by a teacher or pupil to present a personal perspective, for example on the Christian hope of life after death, then that is a different matter, so long as it is clearly presented as a personal view open to discussion and debate.

In summary then, AIDS is a terrible disease, likely to kill a great number of young people, spread by a virus through sharing needles or sex with infected people. It hits us in two areas where we feel vulnerable, our morality and our mortality, and makes us question what we do and what we are. Now is the time for action.

9

Time for Action

The first thing you may need to do is sort yourself out. I find it depressing to see how many young people or older people only really work out the meaning of their lives when their lives are almost over. Will it take a terminal diagnosis for you before you put your own house in order? Urgent decisions may need to be made to change your sex life or stop injecting drugs, as well as to work out what is important to you.

What is important to you?

What will really make you happy in the long term? Who are your most important relationships? I don't mean this year, but over the next few years and for the future. Do you know who your real friends are and to whom you belong?

These are important questions. Many people say after becoming Christians: 'If only I had known before what I know now, my life would never have been in such a mess.' The tragedy is that it often takes a terminal diagnosis, or a near fatal accident, to bring someone to a full stop for long enough to think and feel straight. Most people you know are probably content at the moment to hurtle through life from one relationship to another, from job to job, with no long-term plan in mind, just living for a good time today.

People like that often find themselves washed up on the beach. A woman discovers at thirty-eight that the man she has been living with and promised her marriage and children has been cheating with a younger woman for the past two years and is leaving her. A man finds he has achieved the dream of his own business, but at the cost of losing his wife and children. He discovers too that money buys lots of attention but no friends. Another man discovers after a string of relationships that he is disillusioned and is not sure what love is any more.

Living life to the full

You are important. I believe you were made for a purpose and that you will find your greatest happiness in finding that purpose for yourself. Part of that involves starting to live for others. Jesus said that the only way you could find your true self, that is become fully human, is by losing yourself—not by becoming a passive dormat everyone else can tread on, but by letting go of the right to run your life your way, and instead inviting Jesus to show you how to live his way. I believe God has a plan for you and that because he loves you he knows that his plan is the one that will make you truly happy.

The most important part of that plan is that God wants you to know him personally, not as a distant being, but as your friend, and that he wants to give you new power, strength and inner resources which you need to live life to the full. Often this brings inner healing and sometimes physical healing as well.

Getting involved

Secondly, there is some action you can take which will be of practical help to those who have AIDS. You might want to become a volunteer, to offer time to go into the home of someone who is ill to allow that person to remain at home. If you want to do this you will need to go through a training programme. ACET runs church-based training schemes all over the country. The address to write to is at the back of this book.

Practical help

Thirdly, you may want to talk to someone about some of the matters raised in this book. For example, you may be worried that you are infected or that someone you know may be. You can either write or phone in complete confidence to our Youthline. The address and phone number are at the back of this book. Alternatively the National AIDS Helpline runs a 24-hour freephone service. The number is on page 126.

It may be that you would like some more information on the Christian faith. Write to us and we will send you a free booklet.

Let us know

If you have found this book particularly helpful, or you think we have left something important out, please write and let us know. You might even find your suggestions appear in the next edition.

National AIDS Helpline

If you have any questions or concerns on issues relating to HIV or AIDS please ring the National AIDS Helpline:

0800 567123

This 24 hour service is free and confidential.

A Practical Response to AIDS

ACET (AIDS Care, Education and Training) is dedicated to serving people affected by AIDS. Professional staff and trained volunteers are on call 24 hours a day.

Home Care Network
 Trained volunteers
 Practical Assistance
 Nursing and medical support

Hospice Provision
 Accommodation
 Terminal care
 Day care

Financial Grant
 Equipment
 Clothing
 Services

Education and Training
 Professional and volunteer
 Schools
 Churches
 Organisations

For further details of any of the services we provide please contact us.
Director: Dr Patrick Dixon MB BS MA Cantab
ACET
PO Box 1323
London W5 5TF